# THE COMPL___
# GLYCEMIC INDEX
# COOKBOOK
# &
# LOW GI FOOD GUIDE

**Your Personalized Guide to Lose Weight, Manage PCOS,**

**Fight Diabetes & Heart Disease, and Reverse Insulin Resistance with These Delicious Recipe**

## AISHA PATEL

# GLYCEMIC INDEX

| LOW | MEDIUM | HIGH |
|---|---|---|

### Disclaimer

The information contained in this book is intended for general educational purposes only and should not be interpreted as medical advice. It is not a substitute for professional medical diagnosis, treatment, or advice.

The recipes and meal plans in this book are not a one-size-fits-all solution and may need to be adapted to meet your individual needs, preferences, and dietary restrictions.

It is important to listen to your body and adjust your intake and activity levels accordingly.

Individual results may vary, and this book does not guarantee weight loss, management of PCOS, or prevention or reversal of diabetes or heart disease.

The authors and publisher of this book disclaim any responsibility for any adverse effects that may result from the use of the information contained herein.

Always prioritize your health and well-being. Seek professional guidance when needed and make informed decisions about your diet and lifestyle in collaboration with your healthcare provider.

Enjoy this delicious journey through the world of the glycemic index, but do so responsibly and with your health as the top priority!

Dear valued reader,

I would like to extend a heartfelt thank you for purchasing my cookbook. It brings me great joy to know that my recipes are being enjoyed in your home.

If you have a moment, I would greatly appreciate it if you could leave a review of my cookbook on the platform where you purchased it.

Your feedback will not only help me improve my recipes, but it will also assist others in deciding if this cookbook is right for them.

Thank you again for your support and for allowing me to share my love of cooking with you.


Sincerely,


Aisha Patel

# TABLE OF CONTENT

## Table of Content

# Introduction

## What is the Glycemic Index and Why is it Important?

The Glycemic Index (GI) is like the fuel gauge of a well-tuned sports vehicle that your body uses to navigate the curves and turns of everyday life. The Glycemic Index (GI) is a tool for assessing the rate of impact of carbs on blood sugar levels. Let us dive into a personal narrative to understand its significance.

Imagine you're on the go all day long, and you start with a bowl of sugary cereal (high GI), which is like putting high-octane gas into your car. There is a surge of energy in the beginning, but it quickly fades, and you end up feeling lethargic and unable to concentrate.

Compare that to a day when you choose a low-GI breakfast of steel-cut oats—a hearty choice. It's the same as picking a consistent and dependable gas station for your vehicle. You may take on obstacles without experiencing the ups and downs of energy levels since they stay steady.

Here, the GI plays a pivotal role in directing your food choices toward peak performance. It gives you the power to choose foods that contribute to your health in general, improve your concentration, and provide you prolonged energy. So, by understanding and applying the Glycemic Index into your choices, you're effectively fine-tuning your body's fuel efficiency for a smoother, more enduring ride through life.

## Benefits of a Low GI Diet

**Stable Blood Sugar Levels:** Reduces quick spikes and falls in blood sugar, supporting steadier energy throughout the day.

**Improved Satiety:** Low-GI foods tend to be more filling, reducing overall calorie consumption and benefiting in weight management.

**Enhanced Weight Management:** Supports weight loss attempts by suppressing cravings and encouraging a sensation of fullness.

**Better Mood and Attention:** Maintains constant energy levels, avoiding mood swings and enhancing focus and attention.

**Reduced chance of Type 2 Diabetes:** Helps manage blood sugar, minimizing the chance of developing insulin resistance and type 2 diabetes.

**Heart Health:** Contributes to cardiovascular health by reducing the incidence of excessive blood pressure and improving lipid profiles.

**Balanced Hormones:** Supports hormonal equilibrium, which might be advantageous for illnesses like polycystic ovarian syndrome (PCOS).

**Long-term Energy:** Promotes sustained energy for physical activity, aiding athletes and people involved in regular exercise.

**Improved Digestive Health:** Supports digestive well-being through the eating of fiber-rich, low-GI meals.

**Management of Chronic Disorders:** May assist in controlling disorders like metabolic syndrome, as it tackles crucial aspects such as insulin resistance.

Adopting a low-GI diet can bring about a spectrum of health benefits, ranging from enhanced energy levels to long-term wellbeing and illness prevention.

## Getting Started with Low GI Cooking: Tips and Tricks

Embarking on a low GI adventure can be exhilarating, but managing the initial phase might be stressful. Fear not, fellow GI adventurer! These simple tips and methods will equip you to conquer the kitchen and whip up delicious, healthful meals that keep your blood sugar constant and your taste buds satisfied.

**1. Befriend the GI Food List:** Your first step is understanding which foods fit under the "low GI" umbrella. Invest in a handy GI food list or download a smartphone app to have it readily available. Generally, unprocessed whole grains, fruits, vegetables, and lean proteins are your buddies, whereas refined carbs and sugary indulgences are best enjoyed in moderation.

**2. Embrace the Power of Fiber:** Fiber is your low GI superhero. It slows down the absorption of sugar into your system, keeping you feeling fuller for longer and eliminating those bothersome energy crashes. Load up on leafy greens, healthy grains, beans, and nuts to gain the fiber benefits.

**3. Get Cooking with Healthy Fats**: Healthy fats like olive oil, avocado, and almonds not only give taste and richness to your meals but also contribute to fullness and slow down digestion. Drizzle some olive oil on roasted vegetables, top your salad with avocado slices, or sprinkle almonds on your yogurt for a satisfyingly fatty boost.

**4. Portion Control is Key:** Even low GI foods can trigger blood sugar increases if ingested in excess. Practice mindful eating and pay attention to portion proportions. Use smaller plates, measure out ingredients, and listen to your body's hunger cues to avoid overindulging.

**5. Spice Up Your Life:** Don't let your low GI meals become bland! Herbs and spices are your hidden weapons for adding taste without influencing your blood sugar. Experiment with cinnamon, turmeric, ginger, chili flakes, or your favorite herbs to create foods that tickle your taste buds.

**6. Get Creative with Substitutions:** Missing your favorite pasta dish? Don't fret! Swap spaghetti for zucchini noodles, rice for quinoa, or mashed potatoes for cauliflower mash. With a little ingenuity, you may enjoy all your favorite foods in a low GI style.

**7. Plan and Prep for Success:** Planning your meals and prepping ingredients in advance will save you time and prevent bad choices when you're short on time. Cook a huge amount of quinoa or brown rice on the weekend, chop veggies ahead of time, and have nutritious snacks readily available to prevent reaching for sweet delights.

**8. Don't Go Cold Turkey:** Making abrupt adjustments can be unsustainable. Start by adding low GI items into your existing meals and progressively decrease your intake of high GI foods. This technique will make the transition smoother and boost your chances of long-term success.

**9. Make it a Lifestyle, Not a Diet:** Remember, low GI eating is not just about short-term weight loss; it's about adopting a healthy and lasting lifestyle. Focus on eating great, nutritious foods that make you feel good, and the benefits will follow naturally.

**10. Celebrate Your Victories:** Acknowledge your development and enjoy your victories, no matter how minor. Every healthy meal you prepare and every low GI hunger you fight is an accomplishment worth celebrating.

With these ideas and tricks, you'll be well on your way to mastering low GI cooking and enjoying delicious, wholesome meals that nourish your body and soul. Remember, it's a journey, not a destination, so relax, have fun, and appreciate the flavor of a healthy lifestyle!

# Part 1: The Low GI Guide: Understanding GI Values and Food Choices

# Cracking the GI Code: Making Food Choices with Confidence

The Glycemic Index (GI) assesses carbohydrates based on their impact on blood sugar. Understanding these ideals empowers you to traverse the supermarket aisles and whip up meals that keep your blood sugar level constant. Here's a basic breakdown:

## GI Scale:

**Low GI (55 or below):** These superstars including veggies, most fruits, and nutritious grains induce a steady and mild rise in blood sugar, keeping you feeling fuller for longer.

**Medium GI (56-69):** Fruits like bananas and sweet potatoes, and some starchy grains like white rice, induce a modest rise in blood sugar. Enjoy them strategically.

**High GI (70 or above):** White bread, sugary drinks, and pastries create a quick surge in blood sugar, followed by a drop. Limit these for optimal health.

## Food Choices:

**Prioritize low GI foods:** Fill your plate with veggies, most fruits, whole grains, legumes, and lean protein.

**Pair and Contrast:** Combine low GI carbs with protein or healthy fats. Think avocado on whole-wheat toast or chicken stir-fry with brown rice.

**Mindful Portions:** Even low GI foods might produce surges if overindulged. Practice mindful eating and pay attention to satiety indicators.

**Cooking Procedures:** Certain cooking procedures can influence GI. Steaming veggies or boiling pasta al dente keeps its low GI status.

**Read Labels:** Look for phrases like "whole grain" and "unsweetened" to locate low GI options.

**Going Beyond the Number:** Remember, GI is just one element of the jigsaw. Consider these things too:

- Fiber content: High-fiber foods tend to have lower GI levels.
- Ripeness: Ripener fruits have greater GI.
- Processing: Refined grains and sugars have greater GI than their whole equivalents.

With this knowledge in your arsenal, you can confidently traverse the world of food and make informed decisions that promote your health and well-being. Bon appétit!

# Low GI Food Lists

Ready to go on a low GI journey? Knowing which foods to eat is crucial to keeping your blood sugar levels regulated and your energy levels up. Let's dig into the low GI realm and explore the greatest options in each food group:

## Fruits

**Rockstars (GI 55 and below):** Berries (blueberries, strawberries, raspberries), apples, pears, kiwi, grapefruit, oranges, peaches, plums, prunes, apricots. These fiber-rich fruits deliver sweetness without the sugar rush.

**Moderation Matters (GI 56-69):** Bananas (less ripe preferred), pineapple, grapes, mangoes. Enjoy these in smaller portions with protein or healthy fats for a balanced effect.

**Limit for Optimal Health (GI 70 and above):** Watermelon, dates, raisins, figs. These intense sources of sugar are best enjoyed sparingly.

## Vegetables

**Superstars (GI 10 and below):** Leafy greens (spinach, kale, lettuce), broccoli, cauliflower, celery, cucumbers, onions, mushrooms, peppers. These non-starchy veggies deliver bulk and nutrients without influencing blood sugar.

**Good Choices (GI 11-30):** Green beans, asparagus, carrots, zucchini, tomatoes, eggplant. These adaptable veggies offer moderate GI with vital vitamins and minerals.

**Watch Portion Sizes (GI 31-55):** Sweet potatoes, peas, corn, beets, potatoes. Enjoy these starchy vegetables in moderation and mix them with protein or healthy fats for slower digestion.

**Grains: Champions (GI 55 and below):** Steel-cut oats, barley, quinoa, brown rice, buckwheat, rye bread. These whole grains are rich with fiber and nutrients, releasing energy gradually.

**Moderation Matters (GI 56-69):** Brown bread, bulgur wheat, wild rice, couscous. These options are still better than refined grains but may induce a little larger blood sugar spike.

**Limit for Optimal Health (GI 70 and above):** White bread, white rice, pastries, cereals with added sugar. These processed carbohydrates lack fiber and quickly spike blood sugar levels.

# Legumes

**Powerhouses (GI 50 and below):** Lentils, black beans, kidney beans, pinto beans, chickpeas. These protein and fiber-rich legumes are ideal for adding bulk and nutrition to your meals without increasing blood sugar.

**Good Choices (GI 51-65):** Baked beans, split peas. These products are still a healthy source of protein and fiber, but may have a slightly higher GI.

**Proteins: All-Stars (GI 0):** Lean meats (chicken, fish, turkey), eggs, tofu, tempeh. These protein sources have no effect on blood sugar and keep you feeling satiated.

**Minimize (GI 30 and above):** Processed foods (sausages, bacon), fatty meats (pork belly). These selections can boost blood sugar and contain harmful fats.

# Dairy

**Good Choices (GI 30 and below):** Plain yogurt (Greek preferred), milk (low-fat preferred), cheese (low-fat preferred). These dairy products deliver calcium and protein without dramatically influencing blood sugar.

**Limit (GI 40 and above):** Flavored yogurt, sweetened dairy drinks, ice cream. These options often contain additional sweets, which can boost blood sugar levels. **Good Choices (GI 30 and below):**

# Fats & Sugars

> **Healthy Heroes (GI 0):** Olive oil, avocado, almonds, seeds. These healthy fats deliver critical nutrients and keep you feeling full without influencing blood sugar.
>
> **Minimizers (GI 70 and above):** Butter, margarine, coconut oil, refined vegetable oils, added sweeteners (honey, syrups, table sugar).

# Building Low GI Meals: Plate Composition and Food Combining

Mastering the skill of designing low GI meals is crucial to keeping your blood sugar constant and energy levels high. It's not just about choosing the proper foods, but also how you place them together on your plate and combine them for best digestion and absorption.

## Plate Composition:

**Non-starchy veggies (50%)**

**Protein (25%**

**Low GI carbs (25%)**

**Non-starchy veggies (50%):** These fiber-rich superstars form the backbone of your low GI dish. Fill half your plate with various leafy greens, broccoli, cauliflower, peppers, zucchini, cucumbers, and other low GI veggies.

**Protein (25%):** Choose lean protein sources such grilled chicken, fish, baked tofu, or lentils. Protein slows down digestion and helps avoid blood sugar increases from carbohydrates.

**Low GI carbs (25%):** Opt for healthy grains such brown rice, quinoa, barley, or sweet potatoes. Choose wholegrain versions of bread or pasta wherever possible. Remember to moderate amounts and mix them with protein or healthy fats for slower digestion.

## Food Combining Tips

**Fiber Fiesta:** Combine high-fiber foods including vegetables, legumes, and some fruits (berries, apples, pears) with any carbohydrates. Fiber slows down the absorption of glucose, reducing blood sugar rises.

**Protein Partners:** Pair carbohydrates with protein sources like meat, fish, eggs, or tofu. Protein slows down digestion and helps manage blood sugar, making you feel satisfied for longer.

**Healthy Fat Friends:** Add a drizzle of olive oil, avocado slices, or nuts to your dish. Healthy fats slow down digestion and promote satiety without dramatically altering blood sugar.

**Sweet Success:** Enjoy fruits like berries, apples, or pears as snacks or for dessert. Pair them with protein or healthy fats for increased satiety and to reduce sugar surges.

**Limit High GI Combinations:** Avoid mixing high GI carbohydrates like white bread, white rice, or sugary drinks with other high GI items. This can lead to fast blood sugar spikes and energy dips.

## Bonus Tips

**Mind your cooking methods:** Steaming, grilling, and baking preserve the low GI characteristics of veggies and proteins. Roasting can slightly increase GI, therefore moderate serving quantities if using this approach.

**Spice things up:** Herbs and spices add taste without affecting GI. Experiment with cinnamon, turmeric, ginger, cumin, and more to create tasty and healthful recipes.

**Plan and prep:** Having low GI foods readily available makes it easy to whip up healthy meals throughout the week. Cook a huge amount of quinoa or brown rice, chop veggies in preparation, and have fruits and nuts on hand for handy snacks.

By carefully arranging your plate and strategically combining items, you can make low GI meals that are not only excellent for your blood sugar but also very gratifying and delicious. Remember, it's a journey, not a destination, so experiment, get creative, and enjoy the delightful world of low GI food!

# Low GI Swaps: Make Your Favourite Recipes More GI-Friendly

Craving your favorite comfort food but afraid about the GI impact? Fear not, fellow low GI adventurer! With a few simple modifications, you can transform your treasured dishes into tasty, blood sugar-friendly masterpieces. Here's your guide to excellent low GI swaps:

## Grains

**Ditch the White, Embrace the Whole:** Swap white bread, pasta, and rice with their whole-grain counterparts like brown bread, quinoa, barley, or buckwheat. They improve fiber content, slowing down digestion and reducing sugar spikes.

**Zoodle the Noodles:** Replace pasta with spiralized zucchini, butternut squash, or carrots. These "zoodles" preserve the typical noodle texture while adding a healthy meal of vegetables.

**Cauliflower Magic:** Mashed cauliflower offers a terrific low GI alternative to mashed potatoes. Cauliflower rice also works beautifully in stir-fries and casseroles.

## Sweet Swaps

**Fruit Power:** Replace refined sweets with natural sweetness from fruits like berries, apples, pears, or bananas. You can combine them into smoothies, bake them into muffins, or add them to oatmeal for a naturally sweet taste.

**Spice Up Your Life:** Experiment with cinnamon, ginger, nutmeg, and other spices to add sweetness and richness to your recipes without relying on sugar.

**Honey in Moderation:** Use raw honey sparingly as a sweetener. While it has a lower GI than sugar, it's still a strong source of carbohydrates and should be used in moderation.

**Proteins:** Lean and Mean: Opt for lean protein sources like chicken, fish, turkey, or tofu instead of fatty meats or processed choices like sausages. Lean proteins keep you feeling full without impacting blood sugar levels.

**Beans as Burgers:** Swap beef burgers for lentil or black bean burgers. These plant-based solutions are filled with protein and fiber, keeping you satisfied with a lower GI impact.

## Veggies and Fats

**Load Up on Leafy Greens:** Fill your plate with non-starchy veggies like spinach, kale, broccoli, and bell peppers. They're low in GI and contribute heft, vitamins, and minerals to your diet.

**Healthy Fats are Friends:** Drizzle olive oil, avocado slices, or nuts on your meals. Healthy fats slow down digestion and promote satiety without dramatically influencing blood sugar.

## Recipe Tweaks

**Reduce Cooking Time:** Overcooking starchy foods like potatoes and pasta can increase their GI. Aim for al dente or slightly undercooked for a lower GI impact.

**Cooling Matters:** Cooling cooked rice or pasta before reheating or eating can somewhat lower their GI. This enables for re-crystallization of the starch, making it less readily digested.

**Portion Control is Key:** Even low GI foods can create havoc if overindulged. Practice attentive eating, utilize smaller plates, and heed to your body's hunger cues.

**Remember:** These are only a few beginning points. With a little imagination and trial, you can make practically any recipe more low GI-friendly. Embrace the swaps, discover new ingredients, and most importantly, have fun creating tasty and healthful recipes that work for you!

Bon appétit, explorer! May your low GI path be blessed with flavor and well-being.

# Essential Kitchen Tools & Pantry Staples for Low GI Cooking

Embarking on a low GI journey doesn't require a major kitchen renovation, but stocking up on several important tools and pantry staples will set you up for success. Here's your crucial guide to cooking delicious and blood sugar-friendly meals:

## Cooking Tools

**Sharp Knives & Cutting Boards:** These are crucial for prepping vegetables, fruits, and lean proteins — the cornerstones of low GI cookery. Invest in top quality knives and maintain them for efficient and safe cutting.

**Spiralizer:** Transform veggies like zucchini, butternut squash, and carrots into "zoodles" — a delectable low GI substitute for pasta.

**Blender or Food Processor:** Whipping up smoothies, pureeing soups, and grinding nuts and seeds are a breeze with this multipurpose appliance.

**Large Pot & Steamer Basket:** Steaming veggies keeps their low GI characteristics and releases their vivid flavors. Look for a pot with a steamer basket for convenient cooking.

**Baking Pans & Baking Sheets:** Low GI baking is a joy with the correct instruments. Consider a silicone baking sheet for healthy fat-free cooking and muffin pans for generating protein-packed muffins or vegetarian frittatas.

## Pantry Staples

**Whole Grains:** Stock up on quinoa, brown rice, barley, buckwheat, and whole-wheat bread for flexible low GI carbohydrate options.

**Legumes:** Lentils, black beans, kidney beans, and chickpeas are protein and fiber powerhouses, great for adding bulk and nutrients to meals.

**Nuts & Seeds:** Almonds, walnuts, chia seeds, and pumpkin seeds give healthful fats, protein, and critical nutrients. Enjoy them as snacks or sprinkle them on salads and yogurt.

**Olive Oil & Vinegar:** A good quality olive oil adds healthful fats and taste to your recipes, while vinegar brings acidity and brightness. Opt for balsamic or apple cider vinegar for additional health advantages.

**Spices & Herbs:** Experiment with cinnamon, ginger, turmeric, cumin, chili flakes, and herbs like basil, parsley, and oregano to increase the flavor of your food without altering GI.

**Low GI Fruits:** Berries, apples, pears, and grapefruit are all terrific alternatives for adding sweetness and nutrients to your meals and snacks.

**Non-Starchy Vegetables:** Keep your fridge stocked with leafy greens, broccoli, cauliflower, peppers, zucchini, cucumbers, and onions. These low GI veggies are the foundation of healthy and enjoyable meals.

## Bonus Tips

- Invest in reusable food storage containers for meal prep and keeping leftovers.
- Keep fresh herbs in a mason jar filled with water for easy access and extended shelf life.
- Store nuts and seeds in sealed containers in the fridge or pantry to prevent them from getting rancid.

Remember, the key to success is not about having expensive equipment or a million ingredients. Choose equipment and staples that suit your cooking style and budget, and focus on preparing simple, delicious, and fulfilling meals that support your low GI quest. Bon appétit!

# Part 2: Low GI Recipes

# Breakfast

## Low GI Porridge Variations

Porridge doesn't have to be a tasteless breakfast staple. With a few clever modifications and interesting ingredients, you can transform it into a low GI, flavor-packed masterpiece that keeps you refreshed and satiated all morning long. Let's explore some great variations:

Base Recipe:

**Ingredients:**

½ cup rolled oats (steel-cut oats for even lowest GI)

1 cup unsweetened almond milk (or another low GI milk option)

¼ cup water (adjust for desired consistency)

¼ teaspoon cinnamon

Pinch of salt

**Instructions:**

1. Combine all ingredients in a saucepan.
2. Bring to a boil, then decrease heat and simmer for 15-20 minutes, stirring regularly, until desired texture is obtained.
3. Add toppings of your choosing and enjoy!

**Flavor Adventures:**

Berry Burst: Top with a mix of fresh or frozen berries (blueberries, raspberries, strawberries) and a drizzle of honey for a naturally sweet and antioxidant-rich boost.

**Bonus:** Sprinkle with chia seeds for additional fiber and omega-3 lipids.

**Tropical Bliss:**

1. Blend ½ a ripe mango with ½ cup plain Greek yogurt for a creamy mango sauce.
2. Top your porridge with the sauce, sliced banana, and sprinkle with toasted coconut flakes for a taste of paradise.

**Bonus:** Drizzle with a teaspoon of lime juice for an added pop of flavor.

**Nutty Crunch:**

1. Toast chopped almonds, walnuts, or pecans in a dry skillet until aromatic.
2. Fold them into your porridge along with a spoonful of nut butter (almond, peanut, or cashew) for a protein and healthy fat punch.

**Bonus:** Add a drizzle of maple syrup for a bit of sweetness.

**Savory Surprise:**

1. Swap almond milk for vegetable broth and eliminate the cinnamon.
2. Stir in sautéed mushrooms, chopped spinach, and a sprinkling of Gruyère cheese for a flavorful and filling breakfast.

**Bonus:** Drizzle with a teaspoon of olive oil and top with a poached egg for added protein.

**Spice it Up:**

1. Add a pinch of turmeric, ginger, and/or cardamom to your basic recipe for a warm and soothing Indian-inspired variation.
2. Top with sliced apple, dried cranberries, and a few pumpkin seeds for added texture and taste.

**Bonus:** Drizzle with a teaspoon of coconut oil for a tropical touch.

**Remember:** Keep serving sizes moderate for optimal blood sugar control.

Use natural sweets like fruits, honey, or maple syrup sparingly.

Experiment with different toppings and spices to find your favorite combinations.

Get creative! The possibilities for delicious and low GI oatmeal varieties are boundless.

Happy low GI breakfast travels!

# Savory Scrambled Eggs with Spinach and Feta

This recipe is not just a classic breakfast dish, it's a flavor explosion for any meal of the day. The creamy eggs, colorful spinach, and tangy feta blend together for a pleasant and healthy mouthful that keeps you energized and happy.

## Ingredients:

- 2 big eggs
- 1 tablespoon milk (any kind, including dairy-free alternatives)
- Pinch of salt and black pepper
- 1 tablespoon olive oil
- 1/2 cup chopped spinach
- 1/4 cup crumbled feta cheese
- Freshly chopped parsley (optional, for garnish)
- Crusty bread (optional, for serving)

## Instructions:

**Prep the eggs:** In a bowl, whisk together the eggs, milk, salt, and pepper until well blended. Set aside.

**Sauté the spinach:** Heat the olive oil in a non-stick pan over medium heat. Add the chopped spinach and simmer for 1-2 minutes, stirring periodically, until wilted and slightly colored.

**Scramble the eggs:** Pour the egg mixture into the pan with the spinach. Use a spatula to gently fold the eggs inwards as they cook, generating huge fluffy curds. Don't overcook — you want the eggs to be slightly wet for excellent texture.

**Finish with feta:** Once the eggs have almost set, crumble in the feta cheese and gently mix it in. This will distribute the salty goodness throughout the dish.

**Serve and enjoy:** Transfer the scrambled eggs to a plate. Garnish with freshly chopped parsley if preferred. Serve with fresh bread for dipping or mopping up the lovely runny yolk.

## Tips:

- For a deeper flavor, add a tablespoon of grated Parmesan cheese along with the feta.
- Want some spiciness? Add a pinch of red pepper flakes while sautéing the spinach.
- For a creamier texture, use heavy cream instead of milk.
- Leftovers can be stored in an airtight container in the refrigerator for up to 2 days. Reheat gently in a pan or microwave.

## Variations:

- Get creative with the vegetables! Swap the spinach for chopped kale, mushrooms, or bell peppers.
- Add protein boost by tossing in diced ham, crumbled bacon, or shredded chicken.
- Make it Mediterranean by adding sliced olives, sun-dried tomatoes, and a sprinkle of oregano.
- Go Indian with a touch of turmeric and curry powder.

No matter how you choose to modify it, this recipe for Savory Scrambled Eggs with Spinach and Feta is likely to become a favorite in your kitchen. Enjoy!

# Yogurt Bowls with Berries and Nuts

Yogurt bowls are a quick and easy breakfast or snack alternative, but they can also be a canvas for culinary creativity. This recipe highlights the right combination of creamy yogurt, juicy berries, and crunchy almonds, producing a taste and texture fiesta that's both delicious and healthful for you.

**Ingredients:**

- 1 cup plain Greek yogurt (low-fat or full-fat depends on your desire)
- 1/2 cup mixed berries (fresh or frozen)
- 1/4 cup chopped nuts (almonds, walnuts, pecans, or a mix)
- 1 tablespoon honey or maple syrup (optional)
- Pinch of cinnamon (optional)
- Extra toppings (optional): seeds (chia, flax, pumpkin), oats, shredded coconut, fresh mint leaves

**Instructions:**

**Prep the base:** Pour the yogurt into a bowl. If using honey or maple syrup, sprinkle it over the yogurt and gently stir it in for a delicate sweetness. Sprinkle the cinnamon on top (optional).

**Layer the berries:** Wash and slice the berries (if using fresh berries) and gently set them on top of the yogurt. Frozen berries can be added directly from the freezer.

**Add the crunch:** Sprinkle the chopped nuts over the berries, creating a textural contrast.

**Get creative with extra toppings:** This is where you can personalize your bowl! Add a sprinkle of your favorite seeds for extra omega-3s, granola for a little more sweetness and crunch, shredded coconut for a tropical twist, or fresh mint leaves for a refreshing touch.

**Dig in and enjoy!** Grab a spoon and relish the combination of creamy yogurt, tangy berries, and nutty crunch. It's a simple meal that packs a taste punch and nourishes your body and soul.

**Tips:**

- For a thicker yogurt base, try Greek yogurt. For a thinner consistency, you can add a dash of milk or water.
- Adjust the sweetness to your preference. Feel free to skip the honey or maple syrup altogether if you prefer a more natural flavor.
- Choose nuts based on your taste and dietary needs. Almonds are rich in Vitamin E, walnuts are high in omega-3s, and pecans provide a hint of buttery richness.
- Play with different berry combos! Blueberries and raspberries lend a tangy sweetness, while strawberries and cherries create a brighter flavor.
- Get seasonal! Use fresh berries while they're in peak season for the maximum flavor and nutritional benefits.

With its limitless options for customization, this recipe for Yogurt Bowls with Berries and Nuts is likely to become a go-to in your healthy and tasty repertoire. So get creative, mix and match flavors, and enjoy this refreshing and healthy treat!

## Whole Wheat Pancakes with Cinnamon Apples

These pancakes are not just a great start to your day, they're a celebration of autumn's bounty. Fluffy whole wheat batter embraces bits of warm, spiced apples, producing a flavor and textural combo that's irresistible. So grab your apron and warm the griddle — it's pancake time!

**Ingredients:**

For the Pancakes:
- 1 cup whole wheat flour
- 1 teaspoon baking powder
- 1/2 teaspoon baking soda
- 1/4 teaspoon salt
- 1 tablespoon brown sugar
- 1 cup buttermilk
- 1 egg, lightly beaten
- 1 tablespoon melted butter
- 1 teaspoon vanilla extract

For the Cinnamon Apples:
- 2 apples (any variety, peeled & chopped)
- 2 tablespoons butter
- 2 teaspoons brown sugar
- 1/2 teaspoon ground cinnamon
- Pinch of nutmeg (optional)

**Instructions:**

**Make the pancake batter:** In a large bowl, whisk together the flour, baking powder, baking soda, salt, and brown sugar.

In a separate basin, combine the buttermilk, egg, melted butter, and vanilla extract.

Add the wet ingredients to the dry ones and whisk gently until just incorporated. Be careful not to overmix, as this can make the pancakes tough.

**Prepare the cinnamon apples:** In a frying pan over medium heat, melt the butter. Add the diced apples and simmer for 5-7 minutes, until softened and slightly golden.

Stir in the brown sugar, cinnamon, and nutmeg (if using). Cook for another minute until aromatic and the sugar melts. Remove from heat and let cool slightly.

**Preheat your griddle or pan:** Heat your griddle or pan over medium heat. You may test if it's hot enough by sprinkling a few drops of water - if they sizzle and evaporate rapidly, your griddle is ready.

**Pour the batter:** Use a 1/4 cup measuring cup to pour the batter onto the griddle, leaving space between each pancake.

**Top with apples:** Spoon a tiny bit of the spiced apples onto each pancake. Let them fry for 2-3 minutes per side, or until golden brown and fluffy.

**Serve and enjoy:** Stack the pancakes on a dish, pour with additional maple syrup if preferred, and appreciate the warm, comforting aromas of a beautiful autumn morning.

**Tips:**

- For a protein boost, add a scoop of protein powder to the pancake batter.
- Don't have buttermilk? Combine 1 cup of milk with 1 tablespoon of vinegar or lemon juice and let it settle for 5 minutes before using.
- Try swapping the apples with other fall fruits like pears or persimmons.
- Leftover pancakes can be stored in an airtight jar in the refrigerator for up to 2 days. Reheat them gently in a pan or microwave.

These Whole Wheat Pancakes with Cinnamon Apples offer a healthful and delicious start to your day, with autumn's bounty coming through in every bite. So take your fork, assemble your loved ones, and enjoy this warm breakfast masterpiece!

## Breakfast Burritos with Black Beans and Arugula

These breakfast burritos aren't your usual greasy diner pleasures. They're filled with plant-based protein, fresh greens, and a touch of spice, making them a delightful and energizing way to launch your day. So whip out some tortillas and get ready for a delicious fiesta!

**Ingredients:**

For the Black Bean Filling:
- 1 tablespoon olive oil
- 1/2 onion, diced
- 1 clove garlic, minced
- 1 (15 ounce) can black beans, washed and drained
- 1/2 cup salsa (fresh or canned, adjust your spice level)
- 1/2 teaspoon ground cumin
- 1/4 teaspoon chili powder
- Pinch of salt and pepper

For the Burritos:
- 4 large whole wheat tortillas
- 2 cups baby arugula
- 1 avocado, sliced
- 1 cup chopped cherry tomatoes
- 1/4 cup crumbled feta cheese (optional)
- Hot sauce (optional)

**Instructions:**

**Prep the black beans:** Heat olive oil in a pan over medium heat. Add the diced onion and simmer until softened, about 5 minutes. Add the garlic and simmer for another minute until fragrant.

Stir in the black beans, salsa, cumin, chili powder, salt, and pepper. Bring to a simmer and cook for 5-7 minutes, allowing the flavors to mingle. Remove from heat and set aside.

**Warm the tortillas:** Heat a dry pan over medium heat. Briefly reheat each tortilla for about 30 seconds per side, making them malleable for rolling.

**Assemble the burritos:** Spread a liberal quantity of the black bean filling across each tortilla. Top with a handful of arugula, sliced avocado, chopped tomatoes, and crumbled feta cheese (if using).

Roll the burritos firmly, tucking in the sides as you go.

**Serve and enjoy!** Slice the burritos in half (optional) and drizzle with hot sauce if desired. Devour this tasty and healthful breakfast delight!

**Tips:**

- Feel free to change the filling! Add extra vegetables like bell peppers, mushrooms, or spinach. Swap the black beans for lentils or chickpeas for a different protein punch.
- Can't handle spicy? Go lightly on the salsa or find a milder kind.
- For a vegan version, eliminate the feta cheese.

# Lunch

## Quinoa Salad with Grilled Chicken and Roasted Vegetables

This bright salad is a celebration of fresh, nutritious ingredients, presenting a symphony of textures and flavors that will excite your taste senses. Juicy grilled chicken, delicate roasted veggies, and fluffy quinoa come together in a light and fragrant vinaigrette, producing a dinner that's both fulfilling and nutritious. So fire up your grill and preheat your oven, because it's time to dig into this gourmet masterpiece!

**Ingredients:**

For the Salad:
- 1 cup quinoa, washed
- 1 boneless, skinless chicken breast
- 1 bell pepper (any color), thinly sliced 1 zucchini, thinly sliced 1 red onion, thinly sliced 1 cup cherry tomatoes, halved
- 1/2 cup crumbled feta cheese
- 1/4 cup chopped fresh parsley

For the Dressing:
- 2 tablespoons olive oil
- 2 teaspoons lemon juice
- 1 teaspoon Dijon mustard
- 1 clove garlic, minced
- Pinch of salt and black pepper

**Instructions:**

**Cook the quinoa:** Rinse the quinoa properly and cook according to package instructions. Fluff with a fork and set aside.

**Grill the chicken:** Season the chicken breast with salt and pepper. Preheat your grill to medium-high heat and grill the chicken for 5-7 minutes per side, or until cooked through. Let it cool somewhat, then slice it into strips.

**Roast the vegetables:** Preheat your oven to 400°F (200°C). Toss the bell pepper, zucchini, and red onion with olive oil, salt, and pepper. Spread them on a baking sheet and roast for 15-20 minutes, or until soft and slightly browned.

**Make the dressing:** In a small bowl, whisk together the olive oil, lemon juice, Dijon mustard, garlic, salt, and pepper.

**Assemble the salad:** In a large bowl, add the cooked quinoa, grilled chicken strips, roasted veggies, cherry tomatoes, and crumbled feta cheese. Pour the dressing over the salad and toss lightly to coat.

**Garnish and enjoy:** Sprinkle the chopped parsley on top and serve immediately. This salad is a fantastic stand-alone meal or a perfect side dish for grilled meats or seafood.

**Tips:**

- For increased protein, you can add diced chickpeas or lentils to the salad.
- Feel free to customize the vegetables! Use a variety of your favorites like broccoli, carrots, or asparagus.
- Can't grill? No problem! Bake the chicken in the oven at 400°F (200°C) for 15-20 minutes, or until cooked through.

- Leftovers can be stored in an airtight container in the refrigerator for up to 2 days.

This Quinoa Salad with Grilled Chicken and Roasted Vegetables is a monument to the power of fresh, uncomplicated ingredients. It's filled with flavor, texture, and nutrition, making it a fantastic choice for any meal. So grab your fork, assemble your loved ones, and taste the culinary bliss of this healthy and tasty masterpiece!

## Tuna Salad with Avocado and Whole Wheat Crackers

This is not your usual tuna salad. Ditch the mayo and embrace the creamy deliciousness of avocado for a healthier, flavor-packed variation. Paired with crunchy whole wheat crackers, it's a protein-powered, tasty snack or light meal you can feel good about.

**Ingredients:**

- 2 (5 ounce) cans solid white albacore tuna in water, drained and flaked
- 1 ripe avocado, mashed
- 1/2 red onion, coarsely chopped
- 1/4 cup lemon juice
- 1 tablespoon chopped fresh dill
- 1 tablespoon chopped fresh parsley
- 1/2 teaspoon Dijon mustard
- Pinch of salt and black pepper
- Whole wheat crackers for serving

**Instructions:**

In a large bowl, combine the flaked tuna, mashed avocado, sliced red onion, and lemon juice.

Stir in the chopped dill, parsley, Dijon mustard, salt, and pepper until well blended.

Taste and adjust seasonings as needed. The creamy avocado should offset the tart lemon and offer a pleasing texture.

Spread the tuna salad onto your favorite whole wheat crackers. Get creative! You can make open-faced cracker "sandwiches" or pile the salad high for a heartier taste.

Garnish with more fresh herbs (optional) and enjoy!

**Tips:**

- For a spicy kick, add a sprinkle of red pepper flakes or a drizzle of sriracha.
- Want more crunch? Toss in chopped celery or bell peppers for extra texture and nutrition.
- Squeeze in a touch more lemon juice if your avocado is not quite ripe.
- Leftovers can be stored in an airtight container in the refrigerator for up to 2 days. However, the avocado may discolor slightly over time.

## Bonus Ideas

- Serve the tuna salad on a bed of lettuce or sliced cucumbers for a more substantial lunch.
- Fill halved avocado shells with the salad for a fun and healthful appearance.
- Toast your whole wheat crackers for an added layer of crunch.
- Pair your tuna salad with a serving of fresh fruit or yogurt for a healthy and fulfilling snack.

This Tuna Salad with Avocado and Whole Wheat Crackers is a tasty and healthy variation on a classic. It's packed with protein, fiber, and healthy fats, making it a gratifying choice for any occasion. So forget the mayo, embrace the avocado, and delve into this flavor-packed tuna experience!

# Lentil Soup with Whole Wheat Bread

Indulge in a lentil soup unlike any other. For the most coziness with the least amount of effort, stew all of the ingredients in one pot until they reach their ideal harmony of earthy flavors and textures. A hearty serving of this dish, with crusty whole wheat bread for dipping and dunking, will provide you comfort and nourishment. Get in your comfortable jammies, because lentil soup season has arrived!

**Ingredients:**

Just for the Soup:
- 1-tsp. of olive oil
- 2 chopped carrots, 1 chopped onion, 2 chopped celery stalks, and 2 minced garlic cloves
- 1 cup of washed green lentils
- 4 cups vegetable broth
- 1 can (14.5 oz) of undrained diced tomatoes
- 1 teaspoon dried thyme
- 1/2 teaspoon dried oregano
- Salt and pepper to taste

For the Whole Wheat Bread (optional):
- 2 cups whole wheat flour
- 1 1/2 tablespoons active dry yeast
- 1 teaspoon honey
- 1 1/2 teaspoons salt
- 1 1/2 cups warm water (approximately 105°F)
- Olive oil for brushing

**Instructions:**

**Soup:**

Heat olive oil in a big pot or Dutch oven over medium heat. Add the onion, carrots, and celery and simmer until softened, about 5 minutes.

Stir in the garlic and simmer for 30 seconds, until fragrant.

Add the lentils, vegetable broth, diced tomatoes, thyme, oregano, salt, and pepper. Bring to a boil, then reduce heat and simmer for 30-40 minutes, or until the lentils are cooked.

Taste and adjust seasonings as needed.

**Whole Wheat Bread (optional):**

In a large basin, combine the flour and yeast. Make a well in the center and add the honey and salt. Pour the heated water into the well and mix until a dough forms.

Turn the dough out onto a lightly floured surface and knead for 5-7 minutes, until smooth and elastic. Add more flour if the dough is too sticky.

Place the dough in a greased bowl, cover with a damp cloth, and let rise in a warm location for 1-2 hours, or until doubled in size.

Preheat oven to 400°F (200°C). Punch down the dough and form it into a round loaf. Place on a baking sheet and brush with olive oil.

Bake for 30-35 minutes, or until golden brown. Let cool somewhat before slicing.

Serving: Ladle the hot lentil soup into bowls. Serve with toasted whole wheat bread for dipping, dunking, and soaking up every luscious drop.

Garnish with fresh herbs like parsley or thyme for an added touch of taste and color.

## Tips:

- Feel free to edit the vegetables! Add your favorites like potatoes, broccoli, or spinach.
- For a creamier soup, purée a portion of the cooked lentils before putting them back to the saucepan.
- Leftover soup can be stored in an airtight jar in the refrigerator for up to 3 days.
- If you don't have time to prepare your own bread, utilize store-bought whole wheat bread for a delicious and convenient choice.

This Hearty Lentil Soup with Rustic Whole Wheat Bread is a tribute to the power of simple ingredients and slow cooking. It's a meal that nourishes your body and soul, leaving you feeling joyful and pleased. So gather your loved ones, light up the stove, and warm up to this tasty one-pot feast!

## Chickpea Salad Sandwich on Rye Bread

Chickpeas aren't just for hummus anymore! This recipe transforms them into a tasty and protein-packed salad, perfect for a filling vegetarian sandwich on crusty rye bread. It's a twist on the typical tuna or chicken salad, with an unexpected explosion of flavor and texture that will leave you wanting more.

**What you need:**

For the Chickpea Salad:
- 1 (15 ounce) can chickpeas, drained and rinsed
- 1/2 cucumber, chopped 1/2 red onion, finely chopped
- 1 celery stalk, finely sliced
- 1/4 cup chopped fresh parsley
- 2 tablespoons olive oil
- 1 tablespoon lemon juice
- 1 teaspoon Dijon mustard
- 1/2 teaspoon cumin
- Pinch of salt and black pepper

For the Sandwich:
- 2 slices rye bread
- Lettuce leaves (optional)
- Avocado slices (optional)
- Sprouts (optional)

**Instructions:**

Make the Chickpea Salad: In a large bowl, combine the drained and rinsed chickpeas, sliced cucumber, red onion, celery, and parsley.

In a separate bowl, whisk together the olive oil, lemon juice, Dijon mustard, cumin, salt, and pepper.

Pour the dressing over the chickpea mixture and toss lightly to coat. Taste and adjust seasonings as needed.

Assemble the Sandwich: Toast the rye bread pieces if desired. Spread the chickpea salad on one slice of bread. Add lettuce leaves, avocado slices, and sprouts if using. Top with the second slice of bread.

Cut the sandwich in half (optional) and enjoy!

## Tips:

- For a creamier texture, mash some of the chickpeas with a fork before adding them to the salad.
- Want more spice? Add a sprinkle of cayenne pepper or red pepper flakes to the dressing.
- Make it vegan! Use vegan mayonnaise instead of the Dijon mustard in the dressing.
- Leftover chickpea salad can be stored in an airtight jar in the refrigerator for up to 3 days.

- Serve the chickpea salad on a bed of greens for a lighter supper.
- Stuff it into pita bread or naan for a fun and portable option.
- Top it with crumbled feta cheese or a sprinkle of sunflower seeds for extra taste and texture.

This Chickpea Salad Sandwich on Rye is a tasty and healthful way to enhance your lunch game. It's packed with protein, fiber, and fresh flavor, making it a delicious choice for vegans and meat-eaters alike. So get creative, tweak it to your taste, and enjoy this delightful variation on a classic!

## Salmon with Roasted Asparagus and Lemon Dill Sauce

This recipe is not just a supper, it's a celebration of fresh, seasonal flavors. Crispy roasted asparagus meets delicate, flaky fish, all soaked in a vivid lemon dill sauce. It's a symphony of textures and tastes that will tickle your senses and leave you wanting more. So preheat your oven, fire up the grill (or pan!), and get ready for a springtime culinary adventure!

**What you need:**

For the Salmon:
- 2 salmon fillets (6 oz each)
- 1-tsp. of olive oil
- Salt and pepper to taste

For the Roasted Asparagus:
- 1 bunch asparagus, trimmed
- 1-tsp. of olive oil
- Salt and pepper to taste

For the Lemon Dill Sauce:
- 1/2 cup sour cream or Greek yogurt
- 1/4 cup chopped fresh dill
- 2 teaspoons lemon juice
- 1 clove garlic, minced
- Pinch of salt and pepper

**Instructions:**

Preheat your oven to 400°F (200°C).

**Prepare the Salmon:** Rinse the salmon fillets and pat them dry with paper towels. Season both sides with salt and pepper. Brush with olive oil.

**Roast the Asparagus:** Toss the asparagus with olive oil, salt, and pepper. Spread on a baking sheet and roast for 10-12 minutes, or until tender and slightly browned.

**Grill or Pan-fry the Salmon:** Heat a grill pan or skillet over medium-high heat. If using a pan, add a thin layer of oil. Sear the salmon for 3-4 minutes per side, or until cooked through and slightly browned.

**Make the Lemon Dill Sauce:** In a bowl, whisk together the sour cream/yogurt, chopped dill, lemon juice, and minced garlic. Season with salt and pepper to taste.

**Assemble and Serve:** Plate the roasted asparagus, top with the grilled/pan-fried fish, then spread the lemon dill sauce over everything. Enjoy!

**Tips:**

- For a richer sauce, add less lemon juice. For a thinner sauce, add a splash of water.
- Can't find fresh dill? Substitute 1 teaspoon dried dill for the chopped fresh.
- Serve this dish with your favorite sides like roasted potatoes, rice, or quinoa.
- Leftover salmon can be stored in an airtight container in the refrigerator for up to 3 days.

## Bonus Ideas

- Add a sprinkle of crushed red pepper flakes to the sauce for a spicy touch.
- Sprinkle the completed dish with toasted chopped nuts or sunflower seeds for extra texture.
- Drizzle the salmon with a squeeze of more lemon juice before serving for a fresh, crisp flavor.

This Salmon with Roasted Asparagus and Lemon Dill Sauce is a meal that celebrates the wealth of spring. It's simple to create, yet brimming with flavor and elegance. So gather your loved ones, light some candles, and eat this magnificent culinary masterpiece!

# Dinner

## Turkey Meatloaf with Sweet Potato Mash

This meal isn't just a meatloaf, it's a combination of savory and sweet. Juicy turkey meatloaf, seasoned with warming spices, nestles above a bed of creamy sweet potato mash for a taste and texture combination that's simply delicious. It's a comfort food classic with a healthy twist, sure to delight finicky eaters and gourmands alike. So grab your apron, preheat your oven, and get ready for a sweet and savory symphony!

**What you need:**

For the Turkey Meatloaf:
- 1 pound ground turkey (93% lean)
- 1/2 cup rolled oats
- 1/4 cup chopped onion
- 1/4 cup sliced carrot
- 1/4 cup chopped celery
- 1 egg, beaten
- 1 tablespoon tomato paste
- 1 tablespoon Dijon mustard
- 1 teaspoon Worcestershire sauce
- 1/2 teaspoon dried thyme
- 1/4 teaspoon garlic powder
- 1/4 teaspoon onion powder
- Salt and pepper to taste

For the Sweet Potato Mash:
- 2 big sweet potatoes, peeled and sliced
- 1/2 cup unsweetened almond milk (or any milk you want)
- 1 tablespoon butter
- 1/2 teaspoon ground cinnamon
- Pinch of salt and pepper

**Instructions:**

Preheat your oven to 375°F (190°C).

**Make the Meatloaf:** In a large bowl, combine the ground turkey, rolled oats, chopped onion, carrot, celery, egg, tomato paste, Dijon mustard, Worcestershire sauce, thyme, garlic powder, onion powder, salt, and pepper. Mix well until just mixed.

**Shape the Meatloaf:** Gently form the meatloaf mixture into a loaf shape on a baking sheet lined with parchment paper.

**Bake the Meatloaf:** Bake for 45-50 minutes, or until the internal temperature reaches 165°F (74°C).

While the Meatloaf Bakes, **Make the Sweet Potato Mash**: In a saucepan, bring the chopped sweet potatoes and almond milk to a boil. Reduce heat and simmer for 15-20 minutes, or until the sweet potatoes are soft and easily pierced with a fork.

Drain the sweet potatoes and return them to the saucepan. Mash with a potato masher or immersion blender until smooth and creamy. Stir in the butter, cinnamon, salt, and pepper.

**To Serve:** Plate the sliced turkey meatloaf on a bed of sweet potato mash. Enjoy!

**Tips:**

- For a glaze, mix 1 tablespoon ketchup with 1 tablespoon brown sugar and spread it on the meatloaf during the last 10 minutes of baking.
- Add shredded zucchini or grated apple to the meatloaf mixture for added moisture and flavor.
- Want it spicier? Add a sprinkle of cayenne pepper to the sweet potato mash or the meatloaf mix.

- Leftover meatloaf can be stored in an airtight jar in the refrigerator for up to 3 days. Reheat gently in the oven or microwave.

## Bonus Ideas

- Top the meatloaf and sweet potato mash with crumbled goat cheese and minced fresh parsley for a gourmet touch.
- Serve roasted Brussels sprouts or green beans alongside for a balanced and healthful lunch.
- Get creative with the mash! Mix add roasted sweet corn, black beans, or a dollop of pesto for diverse flavor characteristics.

This Turkey Meatloaf with Sweet Potato Mash is a meal that's guaranteed to become a family favorite. It's easy to make, budget-friendly, and brimming with flavor. So assemble your loved ones, fire up the oven, and create a symphony of warmth and taste on your dinner table!

# Shrimp Scampi with Zucchini Noodles

This recipe takes the essence of creamy garlic shrimp scampi and gives it a healthy, summery twist with zucchini noodles. Packed with taste and light on carbs, it's a terrific alternative for a filling and nutritious supper. So grab your spiralizer, prepare your skillet, and get ready to plunge into this delectable combination!

**What you need:**
For the Zucchini Noodles:
- 2 big zucchini, spiralized into noodles

For the Shrimp Scampi:
- 1-tsp. of olive oil
- 2 cloves garlic, minced
- 1/2 teaspoon red pepper flakes (optional)
- 1/4 cup dry white wine (or vegetarian broth)
- 1/4 cup chicken broth
- 1/4 cup heavy cream (or light cream or coconut milk for a lighter option)
- 1/4 cup grated Parmesan cheese
- 1/4 teaspoon dried oregano
- Salt and pepper to taste
- 1 pound big shrimp, peeled and deveined

For Serving (optional):
- Chopped fresh parsley
- Cherry tomatoes, halved

**Instructions:**

**Prepare the Zucchini Noodles:** Using a spiralizer, produce zucchini noodles from your zucchini. If the noodles seem liquid, blot them dry with paper towels to avoid the sauce from getting too thin.

**Heat the Olive Oil:** In a large skillet or Dutch oven, heat olive oil over medium heat. Add the garlic and red pepper flakes (if using) and sauté for 30 seconds, until aromatic.

**Deglaze the Pan:** Pour in the white wine (or broth) and scrape off any browned bits from the bottom of the pan. Simmer for 1 minute, allowing the alcohol to simmer off.

**Add the Broths and Cream:** Stir in the chicken broth and cream (or replacement). Bring to a simmer and cook for 2-3 minutes, until slightly thickened.

**Season and Cheese:** Add the Parmesan cheese, oregano, salt, and pepper to taste.

**Cook the Shrimp:** Add the shrimp to the pan and cook for 2-3 minutes per side, or until pink and opaque. Avoid overcooking to prevent them from becoming rubbery.

**Combine and Serve:** Toss the zucchini noodles with the shrimp and sauce until fully coated. Garnish with chopped parsley, cherry tomatoes (if using), and serve with crusty bread for dipping (optional).

**Tips:**

- For a richer sauce, boil it for a few minutes longer after adding the cream.
- Feel free to customize the vegetables! Add chopped bell peppers, onions, or spinach for added flavor and nutrients.
- Swap the shrimp for scallops or chicken for an alternative protein choice.
- Leftovers can be stored in an airtight container in the refrigerator for up to 2 days. Reheat gently in a pan or microwave.

- Squeeze a lemon wedge over the completed meal for an added bit of brightness.
- Drizzle with a dab of hot sauce for a fiery bite.
- Serve with a side of roasted veggies or a simple salad for a complete supper.

This Shrimp Scampi with Zucchini Noodles is a meal that proves healthy and delicious can go hand in hand. It's light, tasty, and sure to satisfy. So put down the pasta and pick up your spiralizer, because a tasty and nutritious take on a classic awaits!

# Chicken Stir-Fry with Brown Rice and Broccoli

This stir-fry isn't just a dinner, it's a flavor fiesta! Tender chicken dances with crisp broccoli in a delicious ginger-garlic sauce, all atop a bed of fluffy brown rice for a delightful and healthful one-pan feast. So grab your wok, gather your supplies, and prepare to start on a culinary journey!

**What you need:**

For the Stir-Fry:
- 1 tablespoon vegetable oil
- 1/2 pound boneless, skinless chicken breast, thinly sliced
- 1 head broccoli, cut into florets
- 1 red bell pepper, thinly sliced
- 1 clove garlic, minced
- 1 inch ginger, grated
- 1/4 cup soy sauce
- 1 tablespoon brown sugar
- 1 tablespoon rice vinegar
- 1 tablespoon cornstarch
- 1/4 cup water

For the Brown Rice:
- 1 cup brown rice
- 2 cups water
- 1/2 teaspoon salt

**Instructions:**

**Cook the Brown Rice:** Rinse the brown rice in a fine-mesh sieve. In a medium saucepan, combine the rice, water, and salt. Bring to a boil, then decrease heat, cover, and simmer for 45-50 minutes, or until all the water is absorbed and the rice is cooked. Fluff with a fork and set aside.

**Prepare the Stir-Fry:** Heat the oil in a big wok or skillet over medium-high heat. Add the chicken and cook for 3-4 minutes per side, or until golden brown and cooked through. Remove from the pan and set aside.

**Add the Vegetables:** Add the broccoli and bell pepper to the wok and stir-fry for 2-3 minutes, or until just tender-crisp.

**Make the Sauce:** In a small bowl, whisk together the soy sauce, brown sugar, rice vinegar, and cornstarch. Add the sauce to the wok and stir until thickened and bubbling.

**Return the Chicken:** Add the cooked chicken back to the skillet and toss to coat with the sauce.

**Serve:** Plate the fluffy brown rice and top with the delicious chicken stir-fry. Enjoy!

**Tips:**

- For added protein, add cubed tofu or tempeh to the stir-fry along with the chicken.
- Feel free to customize the vegetables! Swap the bell pepper for other favorites like mushrooms, carrots, or snap peas.

- Make it spicy! Add a pinch of red pepper flakes to the sauce or stir-fry.
- Leftovers can be stored in an airtight container in the refrigerator for up to 3 days. Reheat gently in a pan or microwave until warmed through.

## Bonus Ideas

- Drizzle the final meal with a squeeze of fresh lime juice for an added pop of flavor.
- Sprinkle with toasted sesame seeds or chopped cashews for extra texture and flavor.
- Serve with a side of sriracha or chili sauce for dipping.

This Chicken Stir-Fry with Brown Rice and Broccoli is a meal that's as flexible as it is tasty. It's easy to modify, budget-friendly, and brimming with flavor. So take your chopsticks, assemble your loved ones, and experience the joys of a one-pan culinary journey!

# Vegetarian Chili with Kidney Beans and Quinoa

This chili isn't just vegetarian, it's a vegetarian fiesta! Hearty kidney beans and fluffy quinoa join forces with a colorful medley of veggies and spices, cooked in a smoky-tomato broth for a symphony of flavors and textures. So fire up your stove, grab your ladle, and prepare to warm your soul with this healthy delight!

**What you need:**

For the Base:
- 1-tsp. of olive oil
- 1 onion, chopped
- 2 cloves garlic, minced
- 1 red bell pepper, chopped 1 green bell pepper, chopped
- 1 jalapeño pepper, seeded and finely chopped (optional)
- 1 teaspoon dried oregano
- 1 teaspoon ground cumin
- 1/2 teaspoon smoked paprika
- Pinch of cayenne pepper (optional)

For the Broth:
- 2 (14.5 oz) cans chopped tomatoes, undrained
- 4 cups vegetable broth
- 1 (15 ounce) can kidney beans, drained and rinsed

**Instructions:**

Heat the oil in a big pot or Dutch oven over medium heat. Add the onion and simmer until softened, about 5 minutes.

Stir in the garlic, bell peppers, and jalapeño (if using). Cook for 3-4 minutes, until the vegetables are slightly softened.

Add the oregano, cumin, paprika, and cayenne pepper (if using). Cook for 1 minute, stirring regularly, to release the scent of the spices.

Pour in the diced tomatoes and veggie broth. Bring to a boil, then reduce heat and simmer for 10 minutes.

Add the kidney beans, black beans, and rinsed quinoa. Stir to incorporate and simmer for another 15-20 minutes, or until the quinoa is cooked through and the chili has thickened.

Taste and adjust seasonings as needed. Add extra salt, pepper, or spices to your choice.

- 1 (15 ounce) can black beans, drained and rinsed
- 1 cup quinoa, washed

For the Finishing Touches:

- Fresh cilantro, chopped (for garnish)
- Lime wedges (for garnish)
- Sliced avocado (optional, for garnish)
- Sour cream or vegan yogurt (optional, for garnish)
- Shredded cheese (optional, for garnish)

Ladle the chili into bowls and garnish with chopped cilantro, lime wedges, avocado slices (if using), and your choice of sour cream/yogurt, cheese, or additional toppings. Serve with fresh bread for dipping (optional).

**Tips:**

- Want a thicker chili? Mash some of the beans with a fork before adding them to the pot.
- Feel free to customize the vegetables! Add corn, zucchini, eggplant, or other favorites.
- Make it vegan! Use vegetable broth and vegan yogurt for the garnish.
- Leftovers can be stored in an airtight container in the refrigerator for up to 3 days. Reheat gently in a saucepan or microwave until warmed through.

## Bonus Ideas

- Drizzle the finished chili with a dollop of hot sauce for an added heat.
- Top it with a poached egg for a heartier supper.
- Serve it with a side of brown rice or crusty bread.
- Get creative with the toppings! Experiment with other chopped herbs, cheeses, or even crumbled tempeh.

This Vegetarian Chili with Kidney Beans and Quinoa is a celebration of plant-based goodness. It's filled with protein, fiber, and flavor, making it a delightful and healthful lunch for everybody. So gather your loved ones, crank up the stove, and delve into this gastronomic symphony of warmth and happiness!

# Lentil Bolognese with Spaghetti Squash

This recipe reinvents the classic bolognese, switching heavy pasta for vitamin-rich spaghetti squash and rich meat for protein-packed lentils. The outcome is a colorful dish packed with flavor and texture, great for a fulfilling and healthful supper. So grab your mandoline, preheat your oven, and get ready to embrace the power of plants!

**What you need:**

For the Lentil Bolognese:
- 1-tsp. of olive oil
- 1 onion, chopped
- 2 carrots, chopped
- 2 celery stalks, chopped
- 2 cloves garlic, minced
- 1 cup of washed green lentils
- 28 ounces crushed tomatoes, undrained
- 1 cup vegetable broth
- 1 tablespoon tomato paste
- 1 teaspoon dried oregano
- 1/2 teaspoon dried basil
- Salt and pepper to taste

For the Spaghetti Squash:
- 1 large spaghetti squash

For Serving (optional):
- Fresh parsley, chopped
- Grated Parmesan cheese (vegetarian or vegan)
- Freshly squeezed lemon juice

**Instructions:**

Preheat your oven to 400°F (200°C).

**Prepare the Spaghetti Squash:** Cut the spaghetti squash in half lengthwise. Scoop out the seeds and scrape away any stringy flesh. Place the halves face down on a baking sheet and bake for 45-50 minutes, or until soft and readily punctured with a fork.

Meanwhile, **Cook the Lentil Bolognese:** Heat olive oil in a large saucepan or Dutch oven over medium heat. Add the onion, carrots, and celery and simmer until softened, about 5 minutes.

Stir in the garlic and heat for a further minute. Then, add the lentils, smashed tomatoes, vegetable broth, tomato paste, oregano, and basil. Season with salt and pepper to taste.

Bring the mixture to a boil, then reduce heat and simmer for 20-25 minutes, or until the lentils are cooked.

While the bolognese simmers, take the spaghetti squash from the oven. Let it cool somewhat, then use a fork to scrape out the spaghetti-like threads.

Once the bolognese is finished, combine it with the spaghetti squash strands. Divide the mixture across bowls and serve with your favorite toppings.

**Tips:**

- For a richer sauce, mash some of the lentils with a fork before adding them back to the bolognese.
- Want more spice? Add a pinch of red pepper flakes to the sauce.
- Make it vegan! Use vegan cheese and eliminate the Parmesan.
- Leftovers can be stored in an airtight container in the refrigerator for up to 3 days. Reheat gently in a pan or microwave until warmed through.

## Bonus Ideas

- Garnish with a dollop of ricotta cheese or vegan cashew cream for a bit of richness.
- Drizzle with a little of balsamic vinegar for an added layer of flavor.
- Add chopped greens like spinach or kale to the Bolognese for a dose of nutrition.
- Top with your favorite roasted vegetables for a complete and hearty supper.

This Lentil Bolognese with Spaghetti Squash is a tribute to the delicacy of plant-based food. It's packed with taste, protein, and fiber, making it a tasty and healthful alternative for any occasion. So embrace the power of plants, grab your fork, and delve into this tasty and light variation on a classic!

# Snacks

## Greek Yogurt with Berries and Chia Seeds

This isn't just a breakfast, it's a symphony of textures and sensations that wakes up your taste senses and fills your spirit. Creamy Greek yogurt dances with luscious berries, crunchy chia seeds, and a hint of sweetness for a wonderful and healthy way to start your day. So grab your spoon, gather your ingredients, and prepare to be serenaded by this morning masterpiece!

**What you need:**

- 1 cup plain Greek yogurt (2% or non-fat)
- 1/2 cup fresh berries (blueberries, raspberries, strawberries, or a mix)
- 2 teaspoons chia seeds
- 1 tablespoon honey or maple syrup (optional)
- 1/4 teaspoon vanilla extract (optional)
- Pinch of cinnamon or nutmeg (optional)

**Instructions:**

**Prepare the Chia Seeds:** In a small bowl, blend 2 teaspoons chia seeds with 4 tablespoons of water or milk. Stir and let sit for 5-10 minutes, or until the chia seeds have plumped up and created a gel-like consistency.

**Layer the Parfait:** In a glass or bowl, spoon half of the Greek yogurt. Top with half of the chia pudding, followed by half of the fresh berries. Repeat with another layer of yogurt, chia pudding, and berries.

**Sweeten and Season (optional):** Drizzle with honey or maple syrup, if preferred. Sprinkle with a pinch of cinnamon or nutmeg for added taste.

**Refrigerate (optional):** If you like your parfait cold, you can refrigerate it for 30 minutes or overnight for thicker textures and stronger berry flavors.

**Enjoy!** Grab your spoon and delve into this fresh and delectable symphony of taste and texture.

**Tips:**

- Feel free to get creative with the berries! Use your favorites or a blend for a burst of varied flavors.
- Don't have chia seeds? Substitute with chopped nuts, granola, or even flaxseeds for extra crunch and texture.
- Make it vegan! Use vegan yogurt and plant-based milk for the chia pudding.
- Want more protein? Add a scoop of protein powder to the yogurt layer.
- Top it with a drizzle of balsamic glaze or coconut oil for a distinctive twist.

- For a tropical flavor, add slices of mango or pineapple to the parfait.
- Sprinkle with shredded coconut or chopped dried fruit for extra texture and taste.
- Layer in a dollop of nut butter or jam for a swirl of rich flavor.
- Make it a parfait on the move! Layer everything in a jar with a lid and enjoy it later.

This Greek Yogurt Parfait with Berries and Chia Seeds is a simple yet lovely way to start your day. It's rich with protein, fiber, and antioxidants, leaving you feeling full and energized. So gather your ingredients, unleash your creativity, and make your own symphony of tastes to kickstart your morning!

# Homemade Trail Mix with Nuts, Seeds, and Dried Fruit

This dish isn't just a trail mix, it's an invitation to create! A blank canvas on which you may paint your flavor preferences with crunchy nuts, nutritious seeds, and bursts of sweet and acidic dried fruit. So grab your mixing bowl, pick your favorite ingredients, and begin on a culinary experience that meets your taste senses precisely.

**What you need:**

The Crunchy Base (select 2-3 cups):
- Almonds - classic and versatile
- Walnuts - rich and somewhat bitter
- Pecans - buttery and sweet
- Cashews - creamy and mild
- Peanuts - salty and satisfying
- Pumpkin seeds - nutty and toasted
- Sunflower seeds - large and chewy
- Chia seeds – small and rich with protein
- Flaxseeds - mild taste and increased fiber

The Sweet & Tart Delights (select 1-2 cups):
- Raisins - familiar and always tasty
- Dried cranberries - sour and acidic
- Dried cherries - delicious and chewy
- Dried mango - tropical and juicy
- Dates - inherently sweet and chewy
- Apricots - somewhat tangy and fruity
- Figs - rich and complicated
- The Flavorful Accents (optional):
- Dark chocolate chips - delicious and tempting
- Coconut flakes - tropical and sweet

**Instructions:**

Gather your preferred ingredients and spread them out on a baking sheet. If desired, lightly toast the nuts and seeds in a preheated oven at 350°F (175°C) for 5-10 minutes for improved flavor.

In a large bowl, combine your chosen foundation ingredients. Mix well to spread them evenly.

Add your choice sweet and sour pleasures. Gently fold them in, being careful not to crush the dry fruit.

(Optional) Add your choice flavor accents. Mix well to ensure everything is properly distributed.

Taste and adjust. If you like it sweeter, add a sprinkle of honey or maple syrup. If you want it saltier, sprinkle with a pinch of sea salt.

Store in an airtight jar at room temperature for up to 2 weeks. Enjoy your unique trail mix on treks, as a nutritious snack, or even as a delightful addition to cereal or yogurt.

- Shredded ginger - spicy and warming
- Toasted quinoa - crispy and protein-packed
- Granola clusters - for an extra textural

- For a more fulfilling trail mix, consider a solid amount of protein such nuts and seeds.
- If you're using dried fruit with high sugar content, consider adding some tart options like cranberries or cherries to produce a more balanced flavor profile.
- Get creative with your flavor accents! Experiment with spices like cinnamon or nutmeg, or even add a sprinkling of cocoa powder for a chocolaty touch.
- Make it kid-friendly! Choose creative shapes for the dried fruit and nuts, and add colorful components like raisins or chocolate chips.

**Tips:**

- Feel free to vary with the quantities of ingredients to create your perfect taste balance.

This Homemade Trail Mix recipe is more than simply a snack, it's an opportunity to express your culinary creativity and discover new flavor combinations. So grab your ingredients, unleash your imagination, and design your own delectable journey - one mouthful at a time!

## Bonus Ideas

- Pack your trail mix in small resealable packets for simple on-the-go munching.
- Make a double batch and share it with friends and family!
- Try thematic trail mixes — tropical with mango, coconut, and dark chocolate, or autumnal with pumpkin seeds, dried cranberries, and cinnamon.

# Hummus and Vegetable Sticks

This isn't simply hummus and veggies, it's a flavor fiesta on a platter! Creamy hummus, vivid and crisp vegetables, and a sprinkle of imagination dance together for a symphony of textures and tastes. So take your cutting board, gather your ingredients, and prepare to delve into this dip-tastic voyage!

**What you need:**

For the Hummus:
- 1 (15 ounce) can chickpeas, drained and rinsed
- 1/4 cup tahini
- 2 tablespoons olive oil
- 2 teaspoons lemon juice
- 1 clove garlic, minced
- Pinch of salt and pepper

For the Veggie Sticks:
- A rainbow of your favorite vegetables! Here are some ideas:
- Carrot sticks

**Instructions**

**Make the Hummus:** In a food processor, combine the drained and rinsed chickpeas, tahini, olive oil, lemon juice, and garlic. Blend until smooth and creamy, scraping down the sides as required. Season with salt and pepper to taste.

**Prepare the Veggie Sticks:** Wash and chop your preferred vegetables into sticks, slices, or florets for easy dipping. Get creative with different shapes and colors!

**Assemble the Platter:** Spoon the hummus onto a serving bowl or distribute it on a platter. Arrange the veggie sticks around the hummus, creating a bright and enticing display.

- Cucumber sticks
- Celery sticks
- Bell pepper strips
- Cherry tomatoes
- Snap peas
- Broccoli florets
- Sliced cucumber with radish & herbs for a pinwheel twist

For the Finishing Touches (optional):
- A sprinkle of extra virgin olive oil
- A sprinkle of smoked paprika
- Chopped fresh herbs like parsley, cilantro, or dill
- Toasted sesame seeds or nuts for additional crunch
- Pita bread or crackers for dipping

**Add the Finishing Touches (optional):** Drizzle the hummus with olive oil, sprinkle it with paprika or chopped herbs, and add toasted sesame seeds or almonds for an extra layer of flavor and texture.

Serve with pita bread or crackers for dipping. Gather your loved ones, grab your veggie sticks, and embark on a dip-tastic adventure of flavor and fun!

**Tips:**

- Want a smoother hummus? Add a splash of water while mixing.
- Make it spicy! Add a pinch of cayenne pepper or red pepper flakes to the hummus.
- Feeling adventurous? Roast your vegetables before dipping for a richer taste.

- Customize your veggie sticks! Experiment with different colors, textures, and even pickled vegetables for a zesty edge.

This Hummus & Veggie Symphony recipe is a celebration of simplicity and flavor. It's easy to personalize, budget-friendly, and excellent for any occasion. So gather your materials, let your creativity flow, and delve into this amazing voyage of flavor and texture!

## Bonus Ideas

- Arrange the veggies in a beautiful arrangement on the hummus for a visually stunning dish.
- Serve the hummus and veggies with different dips like baba ghanoush or guacamole for more variation.
- Make separate little platters using small bowls or ramekins for a fun and personalized touch.
- Get creative with toppings! Serve crumbled feta cheese, olives, or chopped sun-dried tomatoes on your hummus for a Mediterranean flair.

# Cottage Cheese with Sliced Cucumbers and Tomatoes

This isn't just cottage cheese with veggies, it's a salad twist brimming with summery flavors and textures. Creamy cottage cheese dances with crisp cucumbers and juicy tomatoes, complimented with fresh herbs and a touch of acidity for a surprisingly light and fulfilling lunch. So take your bowl, stir together the dressing, and prepare to delve into this cottage cheese treat!

**What you need:**

For the Salad:

- 1 cup whole-milk cottage cheese
- 1/2 cucumber, thinly sliced
- 1 tomato, seeded and cut
- 1/4 cup chopped red onion (optional)
- 1/4 cup fresh parsley, chopped (or other fresh herbs you want)
- 1/4 cup fresh basil, chopped (optional)

For the Dressing:

- 2 tablespoons olive oil
- 1 tablespoon lemon juice
- 1/2 teaspoon Dijon mustard
- 1/4 teaspoon dried oregano
- Pinch of salt and pepper

For Serving (optional):

- Whole-wheat crackers or bread for scooping
- Black pepper
- Additional fresh herbs

**Instructions:**

**Make the Dressing:** In a small bowl, whisk together the olive oil, lemon juice, Dijon mustard, oregano, salt, and pepper. Set aside.

**Assemble the Salad:** In a large bowl, combine the cottage cheese, sliced cucumber, diced tomato, and red onion (if using). Gently toss to mix.

Pour the dressing over the salad and toss again. Sprinkle with minced parsley and basil (if using).

Serve immediately with whole-wheat crackers or toast for scooping (optional). Grind some black pepper to taste and garnish with additional fresh herbs, if preferred.

**Tips:**

- Want a fluffier cottage cheese? Add a splash of milk while scooping it into the bowl.
- Feeling adventurous? Add other chopped veggies like bell peppers, radishes, or zucchini for more crunch and flavor.
- Make it protein-packed! Sprinkle on some chopped cooked chicken, grilled shrimp, or even crumbled tofu for a more complete supper.
- Switch up the herbs! Experiment with mint, dill, tarragon, or chives for diverse taste qualities.

## Bonus Ideas

- Drizzle the salad with a splash of balsamic glaze for a sweet and tangy twist.
- Add a spoonful of plain yogurt or Greek yogurt for added richness.
- Pack it for lunch! Layer the salad ingredients in a container and keep the dressing separate until you're ready to eat.
- Make it a salad buffet! Set out all the ingredients and let everyone construct their own individual cottage cheese pleasure.

This Cottage Cheese Delight recipe is a testament to the flexibility and taste of this simple pantry staple. It's packed with protein, vitamins, and refreshing flavors, making it a fantastic alternative for a light lunch, a fulfilling snack, or even a side dish. So gather your ingredients, whisk up the dressing, and delve into this tasty and nutritious spin on a classic!

# Hard-boiled Eggs

Mastering the art of perfect hard-boiled eggs might seem like a mystery, but fear not! This recipe unlocks the secrets of obtaining dependably smooth, vivid yolks and easy-to-peel shells, every single time. So grab your pot, gather your eggs, and prepare to enhance your boiling game!

**What you need:**
- 1 dozen eggs (room temperature, preferable)
- Cold water, enough to cover eggs by 1 inch
- 1 teaspoon white vinegar (optional)
- Pinch of salt (optional)

**Instructions:**

Place the eggs in a single layer at the bottom of a deep saucepan. Pour in cold water to cover the eggs by about 1 inch.

(Optional) Add the vinegar and salt. The vinegar is claimed to help avoid cracks and the salt helps stabilize the egg whites, although both are optional additions.

Bring the water to a moderate boil over medium heat. Do not let the water reach to a rolling boil, since this can cause the eggs to shatter.

Once boiling, immediately remove the pan from the heat and cover it with a lid. Set a timer for 10-12 minutes for properly cooked hard-boiled eggs with a firm yolk.

For a softer yolk, adjust the cooking time:

8-9 minutes for a little runny yolk

6-7 minutes for a very runny yolk (not advised for general eating owing to potential food safety concerns)

After the timer goes off, drain the hot water and immediately pour cold water over the eggs for at least 10 minutes. This pauses the cooking process and keeps the yolks from becoming gritty.

Peel the eggs under cold running water. This makes peeling considerably easier, especially if you added the vinegar (optional).

Enjoy your properly cooked hard-boiled eggs! Serve them simply, dusted with salt and pepper, sliced over salads or sandwiches, or use them in your favorite deviled egg dish.

**Tips:**

- Use older eggs (a week or two old) for easy peeling.
- Don't allow the eggs linger in the hot water after cooking, as this will overcook them.

## Bonus Ideas

- Spice up your eggs! Add paprika, chili flakes, or other spices to the water while boiling for a flavor twist.
- Make deviled eggs! Cut the eggs in half, scoop out the yolks, combine them with your favorite fillings like mayonnaise, mustard, and relish, then pipe them back into the whites.
- Add them to your favorite salads, bowls, or noodle meals for a protein boost.

# Part 3: Sweet Treats

## Low GI Oatmeal Cookies with Dark Chocolate Chips

These cookies aren't just delicious, they're a celebration of nutritious snacks! Rolled oats and nut butter join forces with fiber-rich flaxseed meal and a hint of natural sweetness to make chewy, delightful cookies with a lower glycemic index (GI). So swap out the guilt and take a handful of these dark chocolate-studded pleasures – your taste buds and your body will thank you!

**Ingredients:**
Dry:
- 1 cup rolled oats (not quick)
- 1/2 cup whole wheat flour
- 1/4 cup almond flour
- 1/4 cup unsweetened shredded coconut
- 1/4 teaspoon baking powder
- 1/4 teaspoon ground cinnamon
- Pinch of salt

Wet:
- 1/3 cup natural peanut butter (or almond butter)
- 1/4 cup honey
- 1/4 cup mashed banana
- 1 egg, lightly beaten
- 1 teaspoon vanilla extract
- 1 tablespoon ground flaxseed + 3 tablespoons water (flaxseed egg)

Extras:
- 1/2 cup dark chocolate chips (60% cacao or higher ideal)

**Instructions:**

Preheat oven to 350°F (175°C). Line a baking sheet with parchment paper.

**Make the Flaxseed Egg:** In a small bowl, combine the ground flaxseed and water. Stir and let sit for 5 minutes to thicken.

**Mix the Dry Ingredients:** In a large basin, whisk together the rolled oats, flours, coconut, baking powder, cinnamon, and salt.

**Combine the Wet Ingredients:** In a separate bowl, whisk together the peanut butter, honey, mashed banana, egg, vanilla extract, and flaxseed egg (once thickened).

**Wet Meets Dry:** Add the wet components to the dry ones and whisk until just blended. Don't overmix!

**Fold in the Chocolate Chips:** Gently fold in the dark chocolate chips.

**Scoop and Bake:** Drop rounded spoonful of dough onto the prepared baking sheet, leaving about 2 inches between them.

Bake for 10-12 minutes, or until golden brown around the edges and somewhat soft in the center. They will firm up as they cool.

**Cool and Enjoy!** Let the cookies cool on the baking sheet for a few minutes before moving them to a wire rack to cool fully. Store in an airtight jar at room temperature for up to 3 days.

**Tips:**

- For a sweeter cookie, use extra honey or put a drizzle of melted honey on top before baking.
- Swap out the dark chocolate chips for chopped nuts, dried fruit, or seeds for even more variation.
- Want them extra chewy? Slightly under bake them for a softer texture.
- Freeze any leftovers for a simple and satisfying treat later!

## Bonus Ideas

- Drizzle melted dark chocolate over the cooling cookies for a delicious touch.
- Top them with a sprinkle of flaky sea salt for a sweet and salty contrast.
- Add a scoop of vanilla ice cream and your favorite fruit for a wonderful sundae twist.
- Pack these in your lunchbox for a nutritious and enjoyable afternoon snack.

These Low-GI Oatmeal Cookies with Dark Chocolate Chips are proof that healthy can be delicious! They're packed with fiber, protein, and healthy fats, keeping you feeling full and pleased without the sugar crash. So embrace the guilt-free treat, bake up a batch, and appreciate every chewy, chocolatey bite!

# Banana Bread with Whole Wheat Flour and Walnuts

This banana bread isn't just a classic, it's a taste fiesta! Ripe bananas dance with nutty whole wheat flour and crisp walnuts, spiced up with warm cinnamon and cardamom for a symphony of textures and tastes. So preheat your oven, get your masher, and prepare to bake up a loaf of absolute bliss!

**Ingredients:**
Wet:
- 3 overripe bananas, mashed
- 1/4 cup (60ml) melted butter
- 1/4 cup (60ml) honey or maple syrup
- 2 big eggs
- 1 teaspoon vanilla extract

Dry:
- 1 1/2 cups (195g) whole wheat flour
- 1/2 cup (60g) all-purpose flour (for a lighter texture, optional)
- 1 1/2 tablespoons baking powder
- 1/2 teaspoon baking soda
- 1/2 teaspoon ground cinnamon
- 1/4 teaspoon ground cardamom
- 1/4 teaspoon salt
- 1/2 cup (70g) chopped walnuts

**Instructions:**

Preheat your oven to 350°F (175°C). Grease and flour a 9x5 inch loaf pan.

In a large bowl, mash the bananas until smooth. Stir in the melted butter, honey, eggs, and vanilla extract until completely blended.

In a separate bowl, whisk together the dry ingredients: whole wheat flour, all-purpose flour (if using), baking powder, baking soda, cinnamon, cardamom, and salt.

Gradually add the dry ingredients to the wet components, mixing until just incorporated. Don't over mix! Gently fold in the chopped walnuts.

Pour the batter into the prepared loaf pan and smooth the top.

Bake for 50-60 minutes, or until a toothpick inserted into the center comes out clean.

Let the banana bread sit in the pan for 10 minutes before transferring it to a wire rack to cool fully.

Slice and enjoy! This banana bread pairs nicely with a cup of coffee, tea, or even a scoop of ice cream for a delectable treat.

**Tips:**

- For added moistness, add a dash of milk or yogurt to the wet components.
- Feeling adventurous? Add a handful of raisins or chocolate chips for a new flavor variation.
- Want a topping? Drizzle the chilled banana bread with melted dark chocolate or honey.
- Freeze any leftovers for a quick and enjoyable snack later!

- Swap out the walnuts for your preferred nuts, including pecans, almonds, or even pistachios.
- Add a sprinkle of nutmeg or ginger to the dry ingredients for a varied spice character.
- Make it mini! Use a muffin tray and bake for 20-25 minutes for excellent individual loaves.
- Toast a slice of banana bread and top it with ricotta cheese and fresh berries for a nutritious and tasty breakfast.

This Whole Wheat Banana Bread with Walnuts is a celebration of simple ingredients and tremendous flavor. It's packed with healthful whole grains, crunchy almonds, and toasty spices, making it a delightful treat for any occasion. So collect your ingredients, preheat your oven, and get ready to bake up a loaf of pure comfort food that's as good for you as it is tasty!

## Pumpkin Muffins with Greek Yogurt and Spices

These aren't simply muffins, they're portable blasts of seasonal bliss! Creamy Greek yogurt couples up with colorful pumpkin puree and toasty spices, making soft, moist muffins with a touch of sour goodness. So take your whisk, preheat your oven, and prepare to bake up a batch of magic that's as tasty as it is healthful!

**Ingredients:**
Wet:
- 1 cup canned pumpkin puree
- 1/2 cup plain Greek yogurt (2% or non-fat)
- 1/4 cup honey or maple syrup
- 2 big eggs
- 1 teaspoon vanilla extract

Dry:
- 1 1/2 cups whole wheat flour
- 1/2 cup all-purpose flour (for a lighter texture, optional)
- 1 1/2 tablespoons baking powder
- 1/2 teaspoon baking soda
- 1 teaspoon ground cinnamon
- 1/2 teaspoon ground ginger
- 1/4 teaspoon ground nutmeg
- 1/4 teaspoon salt

Extras:
- 1/2 cup chopped nuts (walnuts, pecans, or almonds)
- Pumpkin seeds for garnish (optional)

**Instructions:**

Preheat your oven to 375°F (190°C). Line a muffin tray with paper liners.

In a large bowl, whisk together the pumpkin puree, Greek yogurt, honey, eggs, and vanilla extract until thoroughly incorporated.

In a separate dish, whisk together the dry ingredients: whole wheat flour, all-purpose flour (if using), baking powder, baking soda, cinnamon, ginger, nutmeg, and salt.

Gradually add the dry ingredients to the wet components, mixing until just incorporated. Don't overmix! Gently fold in the chopped nuts.

Fill the prepared muffin liners with batter, leaving about 1/2 inch of room at the top. Sprinkle with pumpkin seeds (optional).

Bake for 20-25 minutes, or until a toothpick inserted into the center comes out clean.

Let the muffins cool in the pan for 5 minutes before transferring them to a wire rack to cool completely.

Enjoy! These pumpkin muffins are excellent for breakfast, a snack, or even a luscious dessert with a scoop of ice cream.

**Tips:**

- For an extra moist muffin, add a dash of milk or applesauce to the wet ingredients.
- Feeling adventurous? Add a handful of raisins or chocolate chips for a new flavor variation.
- Want a streusel topping? Combine 1/4 cup brown sugar, 1/4 cup chopped nuts, and 1 tablespoon melted butter in a small bowl. Sprinkle on top of the batter before baking.
- Freeze any leftovers for a quick and enjoyable snack later!

## Bonus Ideas

- Swap out the nuts for your preferred seeds, like sunflower or chia seeds.
- Add a pinch of cloves or allspice to the dry ingredients for a stronger spice character.
- Make them small! Use a mini muffin tray and bake for 15-20 minutes for bite-sized pleasures.
- Top them with a dollop of whipped cream and a drizzle of caramel sauce for a truly delectable treat.

These Pumpkin Muffins with Greek Yogurt and Spices are the perfect way to celebrate the warm flavors of fall. They're packed with healthful nutrients, overflowing with pumpkin spice enchantment, and satisfyingly delicious. So gather your ingredients, preheat your oven, and bake up a batch of healthful goodness that's sure to satisfy your taste buds and nourish your spirit!

# Apple Crisp with Oat Topping

Fall isn't just a season, it's a delicious symphony, and this apple crisp is the maestro! Juicy apples sing with warm spices, their melody harmonizing with a crispy, buttery oat topping for a dessert that's as comfortable as it is delicious. So take your apples, preheat the oven, and prepare to conduct a culinary masterpiece!

**Ingredients:**

For the Apples:
- 6-8 medium apples, cored and sliced (select a combination of sour and sweet kinds for extra depth)
- 1/4 cup granulated sugar
- 2 teaspoons brown sugar
- 1 tablespoon lemon juice
- 1/2 teaspoon ground cinnamon
- 1/4 teaspoon ground nutmeg
- Pinch of salt

For the Oat Topping:
- 1 cup old-fashioned rolled oats
- 1/2 cup all-purpose flour
- 1/2 cup brown sugar
- 1/4 cup cold unsalted butter, cubed
- 1/4 teaspoon ground cinnamon
- Pinch of salt

**Instructions:**

Preheat your oven to 375°F (190°C). Grease a 9x13 inch baking dish.

**Prepare the Apples:** In a large bowl, combine together the sliced apples, granulated sugar, brown sugar, lemon juice, cinnamon, nutmeg, and salt. Let sit for 10 minutes to allow the flavors to mingle.

**Make the Oat Topping:** In a separate bowl, combine the rolled oats, flour, brown sugar, cinnamon, and salt. Using a pastry cutter or your fingertips, mix the cool butter into the dry ingredients until it resembles coarse crumbs.

**Assemble the Crisp:** Pour the prepared apples into the greased baking dish. Sprinkle the oat topping evenly over the apples, being careful to cover all the fruit.

Bake for 45-50 minutes, or until the apples are bubbling and the topping is golden brown. Let the crisp cool slightly before serving.

Enjoy! This apple crisp is excellent on its own, but feel free to top it with a scoop of vanilla ice cream, whipped cream, or a drizzle of caramel sauce for an extra luxurious treat.

**Tips:**

- For a sweeter crisp, put a sprinkling of brown sugar on top of the apples before applying the oat topping.
- Feeling adventurous? Add a handful of chopped nuts, like walnuts or pecans, to the oat topping for added crunch.
- Don't have an oven? This crisp can also be cooked in a slow cooker! Simply follow the recipe as suggested, then cook on low for 4-6 hours.
- Any leftover crisp can be stored in an airtight container in the refrigerator for up to 3 days. Reheat in the oven or microwave until warmed through.

- For a fruity variation, consider using other fruits like pears, peaches, or berries in place of apples.
- Drizzle the apples with a splash of rum or apple brandy before adding the topping for a richer taste.
- Add a scoop of dried cranberries or raisins to the apples for a blast of acidity and sweetness.
- Make individual little crisps in ramekins for a

This Apple Crisp with Oat Topping is a celebration of autumn's bounty. It's full with fresh, vivid flavors, delightful textures, and warm, soothing scents. So gather your ingredients, prepare your oven, and conduct this delicious symphony in your kitchen! Let the delightful melodies of apples and oats enter your home and nurture your soul.

# Dark Chocolate Mousse with Avocado

This isn't your average mousse! Creamy avocado swirls with rich dark chocolate, creating a delectable treat that's surprisingly healthful and filled with good fats. So remove the guilt and grab your blender - you're going to whip up a flavor pleasure that's kind to your body and your taste buds!

**Ingredients:**
- 1 ripe avocado, peeled and pitted
- 1/2 cup unsweetened cocoa powder
- 1/4 cup honey or maple syrup
- 1/4 cup milk (plant-based or dairy)
- 1/4 cup vanilla extract
- 1/4 teaspoon salt
- 8 ounces dark chocolate (70% cacao or higher), melted and chilled somewhat

**Instructions:**

**Blend it Smooth:** Combine the avocado, cocoa powder, honey, milk, vanilla extract, and salt in a high-powered blender. Blend until completely smooth and creamy, scraping down the sides as needed.

**Chocolate Swirl:** In a separate bowl, carefully fold in the melted and cooled chocolate until just incorporated. You want streaks of chocolate, not a homogeneous combination.

**Chill and Serve:** Divide the mousse into separate serving dishes or glasses. Cover and refrigerate for at least 2 hours, or until set and cooled.

**Indulge Responsibly:** Garnish with a sprinkling of cocoa powder, fresh berries, or a drizzle of honey (optional). Enjoy your guilt-free and delicious dark chocolate mousse!

**Tips:**

- For an extra avocado kick, use two little avocados instead of one large one.
- Want it sweeter? Add a touch extra honey or maple syrup to taste.

## Bonus Ideas

- Top your mousse with a dollop of coconut whipped cream for a tropical twist.
- Sprinkle on some chopped nuts or seeds for added texture and crunch.
- Serve it in edible cups made from dark chocolate shells for an attractive display.
- Get creative with the toppings! Experiment with fresh fruit, cherries, and perhaps a sprinkle of your favorite liqueur.

- Feeling adventurous? Add a pinch of cayenne pepper for a hint of fire.
- Make it vegan! Use plant-based milk and chocolate for an entirely dairy-free dessert.
- Leftovers can be stored in an airtight container in the refrigerator for up to 3 days.

This Dark Chocolate Mousse with Avocado is a testament to the notion that healthy can be very delicious. It's packed with healthful fats, antioxidants, and the rich, gratifying flavor of dark chocolate. So gather your ingredients, release your inner chocolatier, and mix up this amazing dessert that's beneficial for you and your taste buds!

# Low GI Baking and Desserts

## Carrot Cake Muffins with Oat Flour

These aren't simply muffins, they're small packets of carrot cake paradise! Grated carrots and spicy spices dance with nutty oat flour, creating moist and savory pleasures. And to top it all off, a creamy swirl of cream cheese gives a delectable touch. So preheat your oven, grab your mixer, and prepare to whip up a batch of delectable delights!

**Ingredients:**

For the Muffins:

- 1 cup oat flour (blended from rolled oats or store-bought)
- 1/2 cup all-purpose flour
- 1 1/2 tablespoons baking powder
- 1/2 teaspoon baking soda
- 1/2 teaspoon ground cinnamon
- 1/4 teaspoon ground ginger
- 1/4 teaspoon ground nutmeg
- 1/4 teaspoon salt
- 1/2 cup granulated sugar
- 1/4 cup brown sugar
- 1 egg
- 1/4 cup vegetable oil
- 1/4 cup unsweetened applesauce
- 1/2 cup grated carrots
- 1/4 cup chopped walnuts (optional)

For the Cream Cheese Swirl:

- 1/4 cup softened cream cheese
- 1 tablespoon powdered sugar

1/2 teaspoon vanilla extract

**Instructions:**

Preheat your oven to 375°F (190°C). Line a muffin tray with paper liners.

In a large basin, whisk together the dry ingredients: oat flour, all-purpose flour, baking powder, baking soda, cinnamon, ginger, nutmeg, and salt.

In a separate dish, whisk together the sugars, egg, oil, applesauce, and grated carrots until thoroughly blended.

Gradually add the wet components to the dry ingredients, mixing until just incorporated. Don't overmix! Gently fold in the chopped walnuts (optional).

For the cream cheese swirl: In a small bowl, mix together the softened cream cheese, powdered sugar, and vanilla extract until smooth. Using a spoon or piping bag, dollop little portions of the cream cheese mixture onto the muffin batter in each liner.

Fill the muffin cups with batter, leaving about 1/2 inch of room at the top. Swirl the batter with a toothpick to incorporate some of the cream cheese mixture.

Bake for 20-25 minutes, or until a toothpick inserted into the center comes out clean. Let the muffins cool in the pan for 5 minutes before transferring them to a wire rack to cool completely.

Enjoy! These carrot cake oat flour muffins are excellent for breakfast, a snack, or even a sumptuous dessert with a sprinkle of powdered sugar or a drizzle of honey.

**Tips:**

- For an extra moist muffin, add a dash of milk or buttermilk to the wet ingredients.
- Feeling adventurous? Add a handful of raisins or chocolate chips for a new flavor variation.
- Want a streusel topping? Combine 1/4 cup brown sugar, 1/4 cup chopped nuts, and 1 tablespoon melted butter in a small bowl. Sprinkle on top of the batter before baking.
- Freeze any leftovers for a quick and enjoyable snack later!

## Bonus Ideas

- Swap out the walnuts for your preferred nuts, including pecans, almonds, or even pistachios.
- Add a pinch of cloves or allspice to the dry ingredients for a stronger spice character.
- Make them small! Use a mini muffin tray and bake for 15-20 minutes for bite-sized pleasures.
- Top them with a dollop of whipped cream and a drizzle of caramel sauce for a truly delectable treat.

These Carrot Cake Oat Flour Muffins with Cream Cheese Swirl are a celebration of flavor and versatility. They're packed with the comforting tastes of carrot cake, the goodness of whole grains, and a delicious surprise of creamy cheesecake. So grab your ingredients, preheat your oven, and bake up a batch of these delectable sweets that are sure to impress everyone who takes a bite!

# Dark Chocolate Truffles with Almonds

These aren't simply truffles, they're bite-sized bursts of luxury! Rich dark chocolate melts into a creamy ganache, studded with crisp toasted almonds for a sensory symphony. And the best part? They're surprisingly easy to prepare, using just a few simple ingredients and a sprinkle of love. So take your pot, dust off your cocoa powder, and prepare to make edible masterpieces that are as elegant as they are tasty!

**Ingredients:**
- 8 ounces (226g) dark chocolate, finely chopped (60% cacao or higher preferred)
- 1/2 cup thick cream
- 1 tablespoon unsalted butter
- 1/4 teaspoon vanilla extract
- Pinch of salt
- 1/2 cup sliced almonds, toasted (see instructions)
- Unsweetened cocoa powder,

**Instructions:**

**Toast the Almonds:** Preheat your oven to 350°F (175°C). Spread the sliced almonds on a baking sheet and toast for 5-7 minutes, stirring regularly, until golden brown and aromatic. Let cool fully.

**Make the Ganache:** In a medium saucepan, heat the heavy cream over medium heat until simmering. Remove from heat and add the chopped chocolate. Let alone for 5 minutes, then whisk gently until smooth and melted. Add the butter, vanilla extract, and salt, and whisk until blended.

**Chill and Shape:** Cover the ganache with plastic wrap and refrigerate for at least 2 hours, or until stiff enough to roll into balls.

**Form the Truffles:** Using a teaspoon or your hands, scoop up small amounts of the chilled ganache and roll them into balls. Coat each truffle in the toasted almonds, pressing lightly to adhere.

**Dust and Serve:** Place the truffles on a platter and dust generously with unsweetened cocoa powder. Refrigerate for additional 30 minutes before serving.

**Indulge Responsibly:** Enjoy your handcrafted dark chocolate truffles with a cup of coffee, tea, or as a decadent after-dinner treat.

**Tips:**

- For a fuller flavor, use bittersweet chocolate (70% cacao or higher).
- Want them super smooth? Pass the ganache through a sieve before cooling.
- Don't have time to roast almonds? Use store-bought roasted almonds, but the flavor won't be quite as rich.
- Feeling adventurous? Add a sprinkle of cayenne pepper or orange zest to the ganache for a taste variety.
- Leftovers can be stored in an airtight jar in the refrigerator for up to 2 weeks.

## Bonus Ideas

- Drizzle the truffles with melted dark chocolate or white chocolate for an added luscious touch.
- Roll the truffles in chopped pistachios or dried cranberries for a varied flavor profile.
- Get creative with the toppings! Experiment with sprinkles, edible glitter, or even a coating of coconut flakes.

These Dark Chocolate Truffles with Toasted Almonds are a tribute to the concept that elegance can be simple. They need minimum ingredients and effort, yet give a sumptuous taste and texture that's sure to impress. So gather your supplies, harness your inner chocolatier, and create these scrumptious sweets that are as spectacular as they are delicious! Enjoy them yourself, share them with loved ones, or spread the joy with these bite-sized pearls of pure chocolatey deliciousness!

# Apple Crumble with Quinoa Topping

This isn't your normal apple crumble! Warming spices dance with juicy apples, snuggled beneath a crunchy, protein-packed quinoa topping for a dessert that's as nutritious as it is delicious. So preheat your oven, grab your apples, and prepare to take fall flavors to new heights!

**Ingredients:**

For the Apples:

- 6-8 medium apples, cored and sliced (select a mix of tart and sweet varieties for depth)
- 1/4 cup granulated sugar
- 2 teaspoons brown sugar
- 1 tablespoon lemon juice
- 1/2 teaspoon ground cinnamon
- 1/4 teaspoon ground nutmeg
- Pinch of salt

For the Quinoa Topping:

- 1 cup cooked quinoa
- 1/2 cup rolled oats
- 1/4 cup chopped nuts (walnuts, pecans, or almonds)
- 1/4 cup brown sugar
- 1/4 cup cold unsalted butter, cubed
- 1/4 teaspoon ground cinnamon
- Pinch of salt

**Instructions:**

Preheat your oven to 375°F (190°C). Grease a 9x13 inch baking dish.

**Prepare the Apples:** In a large bowl, combine together the sliced apples, granulated sugar, brown sugar, lemon juice, cinnamon, nutmeg, and salt. Let sit for 10 minutes to allow the flavors to mingle.

**Make the Quinoa Topping:** In a separate bowl, combine the cooked quinoa, rolled oats, chopped almonds, brown sugar, cinnamon, and salt. Using a pastry cutter or your fingertips, mix the cool butter into the dry ingredients until it resembles coarse crumbs.

**Assemble the Crumble:** Pour the prepared apples into the greased baking dish. Sprinkle the quinoa topping evenly over the apples, being careful to cover all the fruit.

Bake for 45-50 minutes, or until the apples are bubbling and the topping is golden brown. Let the crumble cool slightly before serving.

Enjoy! This apple crumble is excellent on its own, but feel free to top it with a scoop of vanilla ice cream, whipped cream, or a drizzle of caramel sauce for an extra luxurious treat.

**Tips:**

- For a sweeter crumble, put a sprinkling of brown sugar on top of the apples before adding the quinoa topping.
- Feeling adventurous? Add a handful of dried cranberries or raisins to the apples for a blast of acidity and sweetness.
- Don't have cooked quinoa? Simply cook according to package instructions before adding in the recipe.
- Leftovers can be stored in an airtight container in the refrigerator for up to 3 days. Reheat in the oven or microwave until warmed through.

- For a fruitier variation, try using other fruits like pears, peaches, or berries in place of apples.
- Drizzle the apples with a splash of rum or apple brandy before adding the topping for a richer taste.
- Add a spoonful of dried dates or prunes to the quinoa topping for added sweetness and nutrition.
- Make separate little crumbles in ramekins for a

your health!

This Apple Crumble with Quinoa Topping is a celebration of fall's harvest, reinterpreted with a healthy twist. It's packed with juicy apples, satisfying quinoa, and a nutty crumble that's both tasty and nutritious. So gather your ingredients, preheat your oven, and take a mouthful of seasonal delight with this crumble that's sure to gratify your taste buds and feed

# No-Bake Cheesecake with Fruits and Berries

This isn't your average cheesecake! It bypasses the oven and celebrates the brilliant colors and aromas of fresh fruits and berries, all snuggled in a creamy, no-bake base. So grab your blender, make up some magic, and prepare to savor a dessert that's as easy as it is delectable!

**Ingredients:**

For the Crust:
- 1 1/2 cups graham cracker crumbs
- 1/2 cup melted unsalted butter
- 1/4 cup granulated sugar

For the Filling:
- 16 ounces (454g) cream cheese, softened
- 1/2 cup powdered sugar
- 1/2 cup plain Greek yogurt
- 1 teaspoon vanilla extract
- 1/4 teaspoon lemon juice

For the Topping:
- 2 cups fresh fruits and berries (mix and match your favorites! Some ideas: strawberries, blueberries, raspberries, blackberries, peaches, mangoes)
- 1/4 cup fruit juice or honey (optional)
- Fresh mint leaves, for garnish (optional)

**Instructions:**

**Prepare the Crust:** In a large basin, combine the graham cracker crumbs, melted butter, and granulated sugar. Mix vigorously until the crumbs are wet and evenly coated. Press the mixture firmly into the bottom of a 9-inch springform pan. Refrigerate for at least 30 minutes to set.

**Make the Filling:** In a blender, combine the softened cream cheese, powdered sugar, Greek yogurt, vanilla extract, and lemon juice. Blend until smooth and creamy. Pour the filling over the cold crust and smooth the top.

**Chill and Set:** Refrigerate the cheesecake for at least 4 hours, or overnight, until set and firm.

**Prepare the Topping:** While the cheesecake chills, rinse and chop your chosen fruits and berries. Toss them together in a bowl with a splash of fruit juice or honey (optional) for extra sweetness and gloss.

Assemble and Serve: Once the cheesecake is set, gently release the springform plate and transfer the cake to a serving tray. Top with the prepared fruit and berry mixture. Garnish with fresh mint leaves (optional) and enjoy!

**Tips:**

- For a deeper flavor, use full-fat cream cheese.
- Feeling adventurous? Add a teaspoon of lemon zest or orange zest to the filling for a zesty edge.
- Want a smoother filling? Strain it through a strainer before pouring it over the crust.
- Don't have a springform pan? You can use a pie plate or another similar baking dish, but keep in mind it will be more difficult to remove the cheesecake.
- Leftovers can be stored in an airtight container in the refrigerator for up to 3 days.

## Bonus Ideas

- Drizzle the completed cheesecake with melted chocolate or caramel sauce for an extra luscious touch.
- Get creative with the topping! Experiment with different fruit and berry combinations to achieve your perfect flavor masterpiece.
- Make it mini! Divide the filling into individual ramekins or muffin tins for gorgeous and portable cheesecakes.
- Top with a dollop of whipped cream or a sprinkle of chopped nuts for added texture and taste.

This No-Bake Fruit & Berry Dream is a tribute to the notion that simplicity can be spectacular. It's packed with fresh aromas, brilliant colors, and a creamy texture that's sure to impress. So gather your ingredients, enjoy the no-bake magic, and create a dessert that's as easy on your time as it is delightful on your taste buds! Enjoy every bite of this vivid fruit and berry symphony, no oven necessary!

# Tips for Low GI Baking Substitutions

Baking scrumptious desserts doesn't have to mean a surge in your blood sugar! Here are some guidelines for making low-GI substitutes in your baking:

Swap white flour for whole wheat flour or whole grain alternatives: Replace half or all of the white flour with whole wheat flour for a fiber boost and reduced GI. Experiment with spelt, barley, oat, or chickpea flour for even more diversity and nutrients.

**Use nut flours:** Almond, hazelnut, and coconut flours are terrific low-GI choices with extra protein and healthy fats. Start by replacing 1/3 of the white flour with nut flour, then adjust based on the recipe and desired texture.

**Add in-fibered flours:** Psyllium husk powder or flaxseed meal can be added in modest amounts (1-2 tablespoons) to boost fiber content and slow down digestion.

## Flours

**Natural sweeteners:** Replace refined sugar with natural alternatives like honey, maple syrup, or date syrup. Use them in lower amounts than sugar as they are sweeter, and remember their GI levels can vary.

**Fruit purees:** Unsweetened applesauce, mashed bananas, or pumpkin puree can give sweetness and moisture while lowering the need for sugar. Start by replacing 1/4 of the sugar with puree and adjust to taste.

**Sugar alcohols:** Erythritol and xylitol are sugar alcohols with minor GI effects. However, use them cautiously as they can cause digestive adverse effects in certain people.

## Sweeteners

## Other Tips:

**Reduce overall sweetness:** Many recipes can be made with less sugar than originally asked for, especially when using alternative sweeteners. Experiment and taste as you go!

**Increase healthy fats:** Adding nuts, seeds, or avocado to your baking can give healthy fats and add to satiety, helping to regulate blood sugar rises.

**Use spices and extracts:** Warming spices like cinnamon, nutmeg, and ginger can enhance the flavor of your baked goods and eliminate the need for added sugar. Extracts like vanilla and almond can also provide depth without raising the GI.

**Control portion sizes:** No matter how healthy your substitutes are, portion control is crucial for regulating blood sugar. Enjoy your goodies in moderation and relish each bite!

Remember, experimenting and finding replacements that work for you and your taste buds is crucial! Don't be scared to get creative and have fun in the kitchen. With these methods, you may enjoy delicious low-GI baked products that are friendly to your health and your blood sugar levels.

# Part 4: Special Diets

# Vegetarian and Vegan Options

## Low GI Lentil Bolognese with Zucchini Noodles

Perfect for a balanced family meal or a fulfilling solo supper, it's a testament to the fact that delicious and nutritious can go hand in hand. So take your pan, embrace the healthy twist, and prepare to make a culinary masterpiece!

**Ingredients:**

For the Lentil Bolognese:
- 1 tablespoon olive oil
- 1 medium onion, chopped 2 cloves garlic, minced
- 1/2 cup sliced carrots
- 1/2 cup chopped celery
- 1 cup green lentils, washed
- 1 (28-ounce) can crushed tomatoes, undrained
- 1 teaspoon dried oregano
- 1/2 teaspoon dried thyme
- 1/4 teaspoon smoked paprika
- Pinch of salt and black pepper
- 1/4 cup water (optional)

For the Zucchini Noodles:
- 2-3 big zucchinis
- 1 tablespoon olive oil
- Pinch of salt and black pepper

Toppings (optional):
- Freshly cut parsley or basil
- Grated Parmesan cheese
- Crushed red pepper flakes

**Instructions:**

**Cook the Vegetables:** Heat olive oil in a big pot over medium heat. Add the onion, garlic, carrots, and celery and simmer for 5-7 minutes, until softened.

**Add Lentils and Spices:** Stir in the rinsed lentils, smashed tomatoes, oregano, thyme, paprika, salt, and pepper. Bring to a simmer and boil for 20-25 minutes, or until the lentils are cooked. Add water if the sauce becomes too thick.

**Prepare the Zucchini Noodles:** While the bolognese simmers, spiralize the zucchinis using a spiralizer or a julienne peeler. Heat olive oil in a large skillet over medium heat. Add the zucchini noodles and simmer for 2-3 minutes, stirring periodically, until softened but still slightly crunchy. Season with salt and pepper.

**Assemble and Serve:** Divide the zucchini noodles among plates and top with the lentil bolognese. Garnish with freshly cut parsley or basil, Parmesan cheese, and crushed red pepper flakes (optional). Enjoy!

**Tips:**

- For a fuller taste, add a splash of red wine to the bolognese while boiling.
- Want a thicker sauce? Mash some of the lentils against the side of the pot while cooking.
- Don't have zucchini? Other low-GI noodles like spaghetti squash or hearts of palm noodles can be used instead.
- Leftovers can be stored in an airtight container in the refrigerator for up to 3 days. Reheat gently on the stovetop or in the microwave.

## Bonus Ideas

- Add chopped mushrooms or bell peppers to the bolognese for added vegetables and flavor.
- Stir in a handful of spinach or kale to the bolognese for a nutrient boost.
- Serve the bolognese over quinoa or brown rice for a complete and fulfilling supper.
- Get creative with the toppings! Experiment with different herbs, cheeses, and spices to get your perfect flavor combination.

This Low GI Lentil Bolognese with Zucchini Noodles is a celebration of healthy enjoyment. It's filled with protein and fiber, low in GI, and bursting with flavor. So ditch the guilt, grab your vegetables, and whip up this delicious and nutritious recipe that's sure to delight your taste buds and nourish your body! Enjoy every bite of this low-GI variation on a classic, knowing you're making a healthy choice that tastes wonderful!

# Tofu Scramble with Vegetables and Turmeric

It's a protein-packed, vegan pleasure that's excellent for breakfast, lunch, or a light dinner. So pop open your turmeric jar, grab some veggies, and prepare to paint your plate with sunshine!

**Instructions:**

**Crumble the Tofu:** Break the tofu into little pieces using your hands or a fork. Set aside.

**Sauté the Veggies:** Heat olive oil in a large skillet over medium heat. Add the onion and garlic, and simmer for 3-4 minutes, until softened. Add the bell pepper and mushrooms, and simmer for another 5-7 minutes, until cooked.

**Spice it Up:** Stir in the turmeric, paprika, cumin, and chili flakes (optional). Cook for 1 minute, releasing the fragrant spices.

**Ingredients:**

For the Tofu Scramble:
- 14 oz (400g) firm tofu, drained and pressed
- 1 tablespoon olive oil
- 1/2 onion, chopped 1 garlic clove, minced
- 1/2 bell pepper (any color), diced
- 1/2 cup chopped mushrooms
- 1/4 cup chopped spinach
- 1/4 teaspoon each: ground turmeric, paprika, ground cumin, chili flakes (optional)
- 1/4 cup unsweetened plant-based milk
- 1/4 cup nutritional yeast (optional)
- Salt and black pepper to taste

To Serve (optional):
- Toasted bread or sourdough slices
- Avocado slices
- Cherry tomatoesFresh herbs like

**Scramble the Tofu:** Add the crumbled tofu to the pan and cook for 5-7 minutes, breaking it up with a spatula to get a scrambled texture.

**Make it Creamy:** Pour in the plant-based milk and stir to mix. Season with salt and pepper to taste. Cook for another minute until cooked through.

**Boost the Nutrition (Optional):** Sprinkle with nutritional yeast for a cheesy flavor and additional protein.

**Serve and Enjoy!** Transfer the tofu scramble to plates and top with your desired toppings. Enjoy on toasted bread, with avocado slices, cherry tomatoes, and a sprinkle of fresh herbs for a wonderful and hearty meal.

**Tips:**

- For a smoother scramble, mix the tofu with a tablespoon of plant-based milk before adding it to the pan.
- Feel free to add other vegetables to your liking! Chopped broccoli, zucchini, or kale are all terrific additions.
- Want a deeper flavor? Use smoked paprika or add a splash of soy sauce or tamari.
- Spice it up! Adjust the amount of chili flakes for a bolder kick.
- Leftovers can be stored in an airtight container in the refrigerator for up to 3 days. Reheat gently on the stovetop or in the microwave. Bonus Ideas: Get creative with the toppings! Experiment with different sauces, spicy sauce, chopped nuts, or vegan cheese crumbles.
- Make it a wrap! Fill whole wheat tortillas with the tofu scramble, veggies, and your favorite toppings for a portable lunch alternative.
- Transform it into a bowl! Serve the scramble over cooked brown rice or quinoa for a complete and hearty dinner.
- Pack it with protein! Add a handful of cooked lentils or black beans to the scramble for an added boost.

This Vibrant Tofu Scramble with Veggies and Turmeric is a testament to the richness and variety of plant-based cuisine. It's filled with protein, fiber, and sunshine-inspired flavors, making it a meal that's excellent for you and your taste buds. So grab some tofu, crank up the turmeric, and create a brilliant dish that's sure to brighten your day! Enjoy every bite of this golden glow, knowing you're making a healthy and delectable choice that fuels your body and your soul.

# Chickpea Curry with Coconut Milk and Brown Rice

This isn't your average curry! It's a colorful dance of fragrant spices, creamy coconut milk, and plump chickpeas, nestled perfectly on a bed of fluffy brown rice. A symphony of flavor bursts with every bite, making it a fantastic vegan and gluten-free option for a full lunch or dinner. So take your spices, enjoy the warmth of coconut, and prepare to make a culinary masterpiece that's as beneficial for you as it is tasty!

**Ingredients:**

For the Chickpea Curry:
- 1 tablespoon olive oil
- 1 onion, chopped
- 2 cloves garlic, minced
- 1 inch ginger, grated
- 1 tablespoon curry powder
- 1 teaspoon ground turmeric
- 1/2 teaspoon ground cumin
- 1/4 teaspoon chili flakes (optional)
- 1 (14.5 oz) can chopped tomatoes, undrained
- 1 (13.5 oz) can coconut milk
- 1 (15 ounce) can chickpeas, drained and rinsed
- 1/2 cup vegetable broth
- 1 tablespoon lime juice
- Salt and black pepper to taste
- Fresh cilantro, chopped (for garnish)

For the Brown Rice:
- 1 cup brown rice
- 1 3/4 cups water
- Pinch of salt

**Instructions:**

**Cook the Brown Rice:** Rinse the brown rice in a fine-mesh strainer. In a medium saucepan, combine the rice, water, and salt. Bring to a boil, then decrease heat to low, cover, and simmer for 45-50 minutes, or until all the water is absorbed and the rice is cooked. Fluff with a fork and set aside.

**Sauté the Aromatics:** Heat olive oil in a big pot or Dutch oven over medium heat. Add the onion and simmer for 3-4 minutes, until softened. Add the garlic and ginger, and simmer for another minute, releasing their delicious aroma.

**Spice it Up:** Stir in the curry powder, turmeric, cumin, and chili flakes (optional). Cook for 1 minute, allowing the spices to blossom.

**Simmer in Flavor:** Add the diced tomatoes and coconut milk. Bring to a simmer and cook for 5 minutes, stirring regularly.

**Add the Chickpeas and Broth:** Stir in the drained and rinsed chickpeas and veggie broth. Simmer for another 10-15 minutes, allowing the flavors to mingle.

**Brighten it Up:** Squeeze in the lime juice and season with salt and pepper to taste.

**Assemble and Serve:** Divide the cooked brown rice onto plates and top with the fragrant chickpea curry. Garnish with freshly chopped cilantro for a splash of color and freshness. Enjoy!

**Tips:**

- For a richer curry, crush some of the chickpeas against the side of the pot while cooking.
- Want it spicier? Add a pinch of cayenne pepper or a chopped green chile to the saucepan.
- Don't have brown rice? Substitute with quinoa or another whole grain for extra fiber and nutrients.

- Leftovers can be stored in an airtight container in the refrigerator for up to 3 days. Reheat gently on the stovetop or in the microwave.

- Serve the curry with a side of naan bread or roti for scooping up the wonderful sauce.
- Get creative with the toppings! Experiment adding chopped almonds, shredded coconut, or a dollop of vegan yogurt.
- Make it a bowl! Add roasted veggies like sweet potatoes or cauliflower to the curry for a complete and hearty supper.
- Turn it into a soup! Add more vegetable broth to the curry to create a warming and comforting soup.

This Chickpea Curry with Coconut Milk and Brown Rice is a celebration of culinary diversity and healthful enjoyment. It's packed with plant-based protein, fiber, and colorful tastes, making it a meal that's nice to your body and your taste buds. So gather your ingredients, embrace the creamy coconut and fragrant spices, and create a taste of paradise in your own kitchen! Enjoy every bite of this tasty symphony, knowing you're choosing a delightful and nutritious choice that nourishes your body and your soul.

# Black Bean Burgers with Roasted Sweet Potato Fries

This is a carnival of textures and tastes, perfect for a backyard BBQ, a family supper, or a satisfying single indulgence. So grab your blender, preheat your oven, and prepare to make a culinary celebration that's as fun as it is tasty!

**Ingredients:**

For the Black Bean Burgers:
- 1 can (15 oz) black beans, drained and rinsed
- 1/2 cup rolled oats
- 1/4 cup chopped red onion
- 1/4 cup chopped red bell pepper
- 1/4 cup chopped cilantro
- 1 tablespoon taco seasoning
- 1 teaspoon smoked paprika
- 1/2 teaspoon ground cumin
- 1/4 teaspoon chili flakes (optional)
- 1/4 cup water
- Hamburger buns (toasted)
- Toppings of your choice (lettuce, tomato, avocado, salsa, vegan cheese, etc.)

For the Chipotle Sweet Potato Fries:
- 2 big sweet potatoes, peeled and sliced into thick wedges
- 1 tablespoon olive oil
- 1/2 teaspoon smoked paprika
- 1/2 teaspoon chipotle powder
- Pinch of smoked salt (optional)

**Instructions:**

**Make the Black Bean Burgers:**

Preheat oven to 375°F (190°C). Line a baking sheet with parchment paper.

In a food processor, pulse the black beans until finely chopped. Don't over-process.

Transfer the chopped beans to a large bowl. Add the oats, red onion, red bell pepper, cilantro, taco spice, paprika, cumin, chili flakes (optional), and water. Mix well to mix.

Form the ingredients into 4 equal patties. Place them on the prepared baking sheet.

Bake for 20-25 minutes, flipping halfway through, until golden brown and firm.

**Roast the Sweet Potato Fries:** While the burgers bake, sprinkle the sweet potato wedges with olive oil, paprika, chipotle powder, smoked salt (optional), and black pepper.

Spread the seasoned wedges on a separate baking sheet.

Roast for 25-30 minutes, rotating halfway through, until soft and golden brown with crispy edges.

**Assemble and Serve:** Toast your hamburger buns.

Place a Black Bean Fiesta Burger on each bun.

Top with your favorite burger fixings! Lettuce, tomato, avocado, salsa, vegan cheese, the options are unlimited!

Serve alongside the Chipotle Sweet Potato Fries for a flavor explosion you won't forget.

**Tips:**

- Don't have a food processor? Mash the black beans with a fork or potato masher.
- Like your burgers spicier? Add a pinch of cayenne pepper to the bean mixture.
- Want even crispier fries? Preheat your baking sheet before adding the sweet potatoes.
- Leftovers can be stored in an airtight container in the refrigerator for up to 3 days. Reheat the burgers and potatoes gently in the oven or microwave.

### Bonus Ideas

- Get creative with the burger mix! Add diced corn, mushrooms, or zucchini for added flavor and texture.
- Make it a party! Serve the burgers and fries with various toppings and let everyone construct their own fiesta masterpiece.
- Turn it into a bowl! Skip the buns and serve the Black Bean Fiesta burgers crumbled over a bed of salad greens, topped with the sweet potato fries, and your favorite dressing.
- Go mini! Form the bean mixture into smaller patties and bake for less time for bite-sized Black Bean Fiesta Burger sliders.

This Black Bean Fiesta Burgers with Chipotle Sweet Potato Fries recipe is a testament to the idea that healthy and delicious can go hand in hand. It's filled with plant-based protein, fiber, and robust tastes, making it a meal that's excellent for you and your taste buds. So gather your ingredients, crank up the fire, and create a gourmet explosion that's sure to delight your senses! Enjoy every bite of this fiesta on a bun, knowing you're making a choice that fuels your body and your soul with absolute delight.

# Creamy Vegan Soups with Cauliflower or Butternut Squash

Dive into a creamy cauliflower dream or revel in the warm hues of a butternut squash symphony. Both cooked to smooth perfection, these soups are rich with flavor and nourishment, ready to fill your bowl with a loving hug. So take your blender, embrace the plant-based magic, and prepare to mix up a culinary canvas that's as diverse as it is delicious!

Base Recipe: This base recipe comprises the backbone of both soups. Feel free to personalize with the cauliflower or butternut squash variants below!

**Ingredients:**
- 1 tablespoon olive oil
- 1 onion, chopped
- 2 cloves garlic, minced
- 1 head cauliflower, florets cut (or 2 cups cubed butternut squash)
- 4 cups vegetable broth
- 1 cup unsweetened plant-based milk (almond, cashew, oat, etc.)
- 1/2 cup nutritional yeast
- 1 teaspoon dried thyme
- 1/2 teaspoon salt
- Pinch of black pepper

**Instructions:**

Heat olive oil in a big pot or Dutch oven over medium heat. Add onion and simmer for 5-7 minutes, until softened. Stir in garlic and simmer for another minute, releasing the scent.

Add the cauliflower florets (or butternut squash cubes) and veggie broth. Bring to a boil, then reduce heat and simmer for 15-20 minutes, or until the vegetables are soft.

Transfer the soup to a blender and process until smooth and creamy. Alternatively, use an immersion blender right in the pot.

Return the blended soup to the stove and whisk in plant-based milk, nutritional yeast, thyme, salt, and pepper. Heat through slowly without boiling.

**Cauliflower Variation**: Add 1 tablespoon lemon juice and a pinch of turmeric to the saucepan before blending for a bright and zesty variation.

Garnish with chopped fresh parsley or dill for a splash of color and freshness.

Serve with toasted crusty bread for dipping or a dollop of vegan sour cream for an extra creamy touch.

**Butternut Squash Variation:** Add 1 teaspoon curry powder and a pinch of cayenne pepper to the pot before blending for a warmer, spicier flavor profile.

Garnish with roasted pumpkin seeds and a drizzle of maple syrup for a hint of sweetness and crunch.

Serve over brown rice or quinoa for a complete and satisfying dinner.

**Tips:**

- For a thicker soup, simmer for a few minutes longer after adding the plant-based milk.
- Feel free to add other veggies to the original recipe, such as carrots, celery, or potatoes.
- Leftovers can be stored in an airtight container in the refrigerator for up to 3 days. Reheat gently on the stovetop or in the microwave.

## Bonus Ideas

- Get inventive with toppings! Experiment with chopped nuts, avocado slices, crunchy chickpeas, or vegan crumbled cheese.
- Make it a bowl! Add cooked lentils, shredded kale, or quinoa to the soup for a protein-packed and hearty feast.
- Turn it into a dip! Blend the soup even smoother and serve with crudités or pita bread for a fun and healthy appetizer.
- Freeze it for later! Portion the soup into freezer-safe containers and store for up to 3 months. Thaw overnight in the refrigerator before reheating.

This Double Dipping Delight dish illustrates that one base can grow into two separate gastronomic excursions. From the light and acidic cauliflower to the warm and spicy butternut squash, each soup is a bright canvas for your distinctive touch. So gather your ingredients, let your creativity run, and whip up a creamy vegan masterpiece that's as adaptable as it is delicious! Enjoy every velvety sip, knowing you're feeding your health and tempting your taste senses with plant-based magic.

# Meal Ideas and Tips for Vegetarian and Vegan Low GI Diet

Navigating a low-GI diet with adopting vegetarian or vegan lifestyle is a delicious journey! Here are some meal ideas and strategies to keep you nourished and satisfied:

## Breakfast

**Savory oatmeal bowls:** Top cooked oats with roasted vegetables like peppers, onions, or mushrooms, along with chopped nuts and seeds for protein and crunch.

**Tofu scramble:** Crumble and sauté tofu with veggies like spinach, tomatoes, and onions for a protein-packed, low-GI scramble. Add turmeric for an added flavor boost.

**Chia pudding:** Soak chia seeds in unsweetened plant-based milk overnight. Top with fresh fruit, berries, and almonds for a fiber-rich breakfast.

**Smoothies:** Blend leafy greens, fruit, protein powder (optional), and unsweetened plant-based milk for a quick and nutrient-packed breakfast. Add spices like cinnamon or ginger for added taste.

## Lunch

**Salads:** Layer a bed of leafy greens with quinoa, chickpeas, lentils, roasted veggies, avocado, and a low-sugar vinaigrette.

**Soup & Sandwich:** Enjoy a bowl of creamy vegan lentil soup combined with whole-wheat bread or a vegetarian wrap.

**Buddha bowls:** Fill a bowl with brown rice, roasted sweet potato, roasted cauliflower, chickpeas, and a tahini dressing for a tasty and satisfying lunch.

**Vegetable burritos:** Wrap various roasted veggies, black beans, and quinoa in whole-wheat tortillas for a portable and delicious lunch.

## Dinner

**Vegetarian chili:** Simmer beans, lentils, veggies, and spices in a fragrant tomato-based broth for a filling and protein-rich supper.

**Curries:** Opt for coconut milk-based curries with chickpeas, tofu, or lentils, served with brown rice or quinoa. Experiment with different vegetables and spices like turmeric, cumin, and coriander.

**Lentil pasta bake:** Combine lentil pasta with sautéed vegetables, a creamy vegan sauce, and bake with a sprinkle of nutritional yeast for a cheesy and comforting dinner.

**Stuffed portobello mushrooms:** Fill portobello mushrooms with quinoa, chopped veggies, and herbs for a substantial and tasty main dish.

## Tips for Low GI Vegetarian & Vegan Cooking

**Focus on entire grains:** Choose brown rice, quinoa, whole-wheat bread, and other whole grains over refined carbohydrates.

**Pair protein with fiber**: Combine protein sources like beans, lentils, tofu, and nuts with vegetables and healthy grains for balanced blood sugar levels.

**Limit sugary fruits:** Opt for low-sugar fruits like berries, pears, and apples. Add sweetness with spices like cinnamon or ginger.

**Choose healthy fats:** Include healthy fats like avocado, nuts, and seeds in your diet for satiety and nutrient absorption.

**Cook using healthy oils:** Use olive oil, avocado oil, or coconut oil for cooking instead of processed vegetable oils.

**Minimize sugar:** Avoid added sugars in processed foods and drinks. Opt for natural sweets like honey or maple syrup in moderation.

**Read food labels:** Pay attention to the glycemic index (GI) of ingredients while buying packaged foods.

**Plan ahead:** Planning your meals and snacks can help you make good choices throughout the day.

Enjoy! Focus on the enjoyment and variety of vegetarian and vegan meals instead of restriction.

**Bonus Tip:** Check out these plant-based cookbooks and blogs for additional cooking ideas and direction!

Remember, the key to a good low-GI diet is to focus on whole, unprocessed foods, emphasize veggies and whole grains, and choose healthy fats and proteins. With a little planning and ingenuity, you may easily enjoy tasty and satisfying vegetarian or vegan meals that fit your low-GI lifestyle. So, let your cooking journey begin!

# Part 5: Practical Strategies

# Meal Prep and Batch Cooking Tips

## Planning Your Weekly Meals

Meal planning can seem daunting, but it's a powerful tool for healthy eating, saving time, and reducing food waste. Here's a roadmap to get you started:

1. Assess your needs
2. Gather inspiration
3. Build your menu
4. Create a shopping list
5. Get organized

plan meals accordingly.

**1. Assess your needs:**

• Dietary restrictions: Consider allergies, preferences (vegetarian, vegan, etc.), and any health goals you have.
• Schedule: Account for busy days and plan quick meals or leftovers for those times.
• Budget: Be realistic about what you can afford and

**2. Gather inspiration:**

• Browse cookbooks, websites, and blogs: Look for recipes that meet your dietary restrictions and taste preferences.
• Ask friends and family about their favorite dishes.
• Check weekly grocery store fliers for specials and seasonal food.

**3. Build your menu:**

• Decide on 2-3 meals per day (breakfast, lunch, dinner) for the week.
• Balance your meals with protein, carbohydrates, and healthy fats.
• Try to incorporate different vegetables and fruits throughout the week.

- Cook once, eat twice: Cook larger amounts of some meals and eat them as leftovers later in the week.
- Consider preparation things in advance (chopping veggies, marinating meat, etc.) to save time on cooking days.

## 4. Create a shopping list:

- List all the ingredients you need for your scheduled meals.
- Include essentials like spices, oils, and pantry supplies.
- Check your fridge and pantry to prevent buying duplicates.

## 5. Get organized:

- Assign specified days for cooking various dishes.
- Prep items on specific days to make cooking times shorter.
- Utilize storage containers to keep leftovers fresh and accessible.

### Bonus tips

- Get creative with leftovers! Repurpose them into new dishes, such utilizing leftover chicken in a stir-fry or salad.
- Involve the family in planning and cooking! It's a terrific approach to acquire healthy habits and spend quality time together.
- Don't be afraid to experiment and try new things! Meal planning is a journey, and you'll uncover what works best for you as you go.

Remember, meal planning is a flexible tool. Don't be afraid to change your strategy as needed throughout the week based on your energy levels, desires, and any unforeseen circumstances. The idea is to make healthy eating a sustainable and joyful habit!

## Utilizing Leftovers

Leftovers can be more than simply yesterday's meal! With a little imagination, you can change them into fresh and tasty dinners, saving time, money, and decreasing food waste. Here are some strategies and ways to utilize leftovers like a pro:

**Think beyond reheating:**

Get inspired by cuisines around the world. Leftover chicken can become tacos with salsa and avocado, a Thai stir-fry, or an Indian curry. Leftover roasted vegetables can be used to frittatas, soups, or pasta salads.

Get creative with changes. Mashed potatoes can produce gnocchi or potato pancakes. Shredded meat can be used in quesadillas, omelets, or stuffed peppers. Leftover grains can be the base for grain bowls or veggie burgers.

**Mix and match flavors:**

Combine leftovers from different meals. Leftover roasted sweet potato and black beans can become a delicious salad with a sprinkle of feta cheese and cilantro. Leftover pasta and cheese sauce can be turned into a comforting mac and cheese bake with chopped broccoli.

Add new ingredients to enhance the flavor. Leftover soup can be thickened with cooked lentils or brown rice. Leftover stir-fry can be tossed with noodles or fresh vegetables.

**Get portion-smart:**

Freeze leftovers in individual portions. This is perfect for lunch or quick meals when you're short on time.

Use smaller storage containers to prevent leftovers from languishing in the back of the fridge. This will encourage you to use them before they spoil.

**Bonus tips:**

Label your leftovers with the date and contents. This will help you remember what you have and reduce food waste.

Get the kids engaged! Let them help you explore fresh options for leftover dinners. This is a great way to teach them about cooking and reduce food waste.

Don't be afraid to experiment! The choices are unlimited when it comes to repurposing leftovers. So have fun and be creative!

Remember, utilizing leftovers is not just about saving money and reducing food waste. It's also a terrific opportunity to get creative in the kitchen and test various flavors. So next time you have leftovers, don't just chuck them in the trash. Get inspired, embrace your inner chef, and convert them into a great new dinner!

# Prepping Ingredients in Advance

Prepping items in advance is a game-changer for anyone who wants to eat healthy and save time in the kitchen. It's the bridge between a hectic weekday scramble and a serene culinary symphony. Here's how you can become a master of prep and boost your cooking game:

**Choose your battles:**

**Identify time-consuming tasks:** Chopping vegetables, washing fruits, portioning proteins, and marinating meats are good possibilities for prep.

**Prioritize convenience:** Prep items for meals you consume frequently or know you'll struggle with over the week.

**Gather your tools:**

**Sharpen your knives!** Dull knives are dangerous and inefficient.

Invest in good storage containers: Airtight containers keep ingredients fresh and avoid smells.

**Utilize prep tools:** Mandolines, spiralizers, and food processors may save you heaps of time and effort.

**Prep like a pro:**

**Wash and dry everything.** This prevents spoiling and makes ingredients ready to use in an instant.

**Chop all your vegetables at once:** Dice onions, slice peppers, and shred carrots in one move. Store them in labeled containers for convenient access.

**Portion proteins:** Pre-measure meat, fish, or tofu for individual meals. Marinate if needed.

**Cook grains in bulk:** Brown rice, quinoa, or pasta can be cooked in large batches and stored in the fridge for quick lunches or dinner sides.

**Hard-boil eggs for the week:** Perfect for salads, sandwiches, or snacks.

**Prepare sauces and dressings in advance:** Store them in mason jars and have them ready to sprinkle or toss.

**Storage for success:**

**Label everything!** Date and identify the containers to avoid mystery lunches.

**Choose the proper container based on the ingredient:** Leafy greens need breathable containers, while cooked grains thrive in airtight one.

**Store strategically:** Place frequently used ingredients at eye level in the fridge or cupboard.

**Bonus tips:**

- Get the youngsters involved: Make preparation an enjoyable family activity to teach kids essential skills.

- Listen to music or podcasts while prepping: Turn it into a mini-me time session.
- Enjoy the process! Savoring the preparation can make cooking even more enjoyable.

Prepping ingredients in advance is all about setting yourself up for success. It doesn't have to be an all-day marathon. Start small, choose your battles, and see how your weeknight dinners shift from hectic to seamless. Soon, you'll be a prep expert whipping up delectable dishes like a seasoned chef, all thanks to a little organized ahead. Remember, every minute invested in prep saves you tenfold in the kitchen, providing you more time to savor the flavors and experience the magic of cooking.

## Easy and Efficient Batch Cooking Techniques

Batch cooking can be your culinary hero, saving you time, money, and stress throughout the week. Here are some easy and efficient strategies to conquer the batch cooking world:

**Choose your weapons:**

**Double or treble recipes:** This is the simplest trick! Simply multiply all the ingredients in your favorite dish and freeze extra amounts for later. Bonus: It often costs less per serving this way.

**Master the base recipe:** Pick a versatile foundation like lentil soup, chili, or tomato sauce. Then, tweak it with different toppings or side dishes each time for variation.

**Go for grains in bulk:** Cook a big batch of brown rice, quinoa, or even couscous. These are wonderful for quick lunches, bowls, and side dishes.

**Roast it up:** Roasting veggies like potatoes, broccoli, or bell peppers is straightforward and makes them very tasty. Use them in salads, wraps, or pasta recipes.

**Prep like a pro:**

**Chop on Sunday:** Dedicate some time on the weekend to preparation veggies, marinating meats, and portioning proteins. You'll thank yourself all week!

**Utilize tools:** Food processors, spiralizers, and mandolines can be your time-saving companions, especially for cutting mountains of veggies.

**Cook once, eat twice:** Cook double the protein (chicken, tofu, etc.) and utilize it in different ways during the week. For example, grilled chicken can be cut for salads, utilized in stir-fries, or shredded for tacos.

**Storage savvy:**

**Invest in nice containers:** Airtight containers are vital for freezing and storing food without freezer burn or leaks. Portion individual servings for convenience.

**Label everything:** Date and name your containers to prevent mystery meals and avoid food waste.

**Freeze strategically:** Place commonly used dishes in the front of the freezer for easy access.

**Bonus tips:**

**Get creative with leftovers!** Repurpose them into new dishes to avoid boredom. Leftover roasted veggies can create a frittata, and leftover soup can be the base for a spaghetti sauce.

**Involve the family:** Make batch cooking a team effort. Everyone can help with prepping, cooking, and cleaning up.

**Don't overthink things!** Start small and choose recipes you already appreciate. Batch cooking doesn't have to be fancy or complicated.

Remember, batch cooking is a journey, not a destination. Experiment, find what works for you, and enjoy the flexibility of having wonderful meals available whenever you need them. So take your ingredients, unleash your inner chef, and conquer the batch cooking world!

## Low GI Meal Prep Ideas for the Week

Get ready for a delicious and healthy week with these low GI meal prep ideas! They're filled with flavor, fiber, and staying power to keep you nourished and satisfied all week

**Monday:**

**Breakfast:** Chia pudding with fruit and nuts

**Lunch:** Salad with quinoa, roasted chickpeas, avocado, and balsamic vinaigrette

**Dinner:** Slow cooker lentil soup with whole-wheat bread

**Tuesday:**

**Breakfast:** Omelette with spinach, mushrooms, and low-fat cheese

**Lunch:** Leftover lentil soup with a side salad

**Dinner:** Salmon with roasted sweet potatoes and green beans

**Wednesday:**

**Breakfast:** Greek yogurt with fruit and granola

**Lunch:** Turkey and vegetable wrap on whole-wheat tortillas

**Dinner:** One-pan chicken stir-fry with brown rice and peppers

**Thursday:**

**Breakfast:** Oatmeal with fruit and cinnamon

**Lunch:** Leftover stir-fry with a side of cucumber and tomato salad

**Dinner:** Vegetarian chili with cornbread

**Friday**

**Breakfast:** Egg muffins with spinach and peppers

**Lunch:** Tuna salad with apple slices and crackers

**Dinner:** Baked tofu with quinoa and roasted

long.

**Snacks:**

Fruits including berries, apples, pears, and oranges
Vegetables like carrots, cucumbers, celery, and peppers
Nuts and seeds (almonds, walnuts, sunflower seeds)
Greek yogurt with fruit and granola
Hard-boiled eggs
Cottage cheese with sliced veggies

**Tips:**

- Cook a large batch of brown rice or quinoa early in the week to use as a base for lunches and dinners.
- Roast a sheet pan of vegetables at the beginning of the week to use in salads, wraps, and stir-fries.
- Make a huge batch of soup or chili on the weekend and enjoy it throughout the week.
- Use leftovers creatively! Repurpose them into different dishes to avoid becoming bored.
- Don't forget to carry healthy snacks to keep your energy levels up throughout the day.
- Adjust these ideas to your preferences and nutritional demands. Enjoy!

# Low GI Alternatives for Common Cravings

## Satisfying Sweets

Fruit with yogurt, dark chocolate, handmade energy bites

Ah, the siren song of sweets! But who says indulgence has to mean guilt? Let's plunge into the realm of "satisfying sweets" that are as excellent for your body as they are for your taste buds:

**1. Fruit with Yogurt and Dark Chocolate:** Simplicity at its finest: Slice your favorite fruits like berries, banana, apple, or pear. Layer them in a bowl with creamy Greek yogurt or plant-based yogurt. Drizzle with melted dark chocolate (70% cacao or higher) for a rich, antioxidant-packed coating. Top with chopped nuts or seeds for extra crunch and protein.

**2. Dark Chocolate Dipped Dates with Almond Butter**: Nature's candy with a twist: Pit Medjool dates and stuff them with a spoonful of silky almond butter. Drizzle with melted dark chocolate and sprinkle with a bit of sea salt for a delicious sweet-salty explosion.

**3. Tropical Smoothie Bowl with Homemade Granola:** A taste of paradise: Blend frozen mango, pineapple, and spinach till smooth. Pour into a bowl and top with homemade granola made with oats, nuts, seeds, and a touch of honey. Drizzle with coconut yogurt and toasted coconut flakes for a tropical vacation in every bite.

**4. Homemade Energy Bites:** No-bake powerhouses: Pulse oats, nuts, seeds, dried fruit, and a bit of natural sweetness in a food processor. Form into bite-sized balls and coat them in melted dark chocolate or unsweetened coconut flakes. These healthy powerhouses will keep you going all day long.

**5. Baked Apples with Cinnamon and Walnuts:** Classic comfort with a twist: Core apples and fill each with chopped walnuts, raisins, and a dusting of cinnamon. Drizzle with a bit of honey and bake until soft and aromatic. Serve warm with a scoop of vanilla frozen yogurt for a comforting fall treat.

**Bonus Tip:** Get inventive with toppings! Consider fresh herbs like mint or basil for an unexpected twist, or a dollop of chia seed jam for added sweetness and fiber.

Remember, "Satisfying sweets" are all about balance. Enjoy these delicacies in moderation and mix them with other meals for a balanced and guilt-free enjoyment. So go ahead, enjoy the sweets, and fuel your body in the most delightful way imaginable!

## Comfort Food Cravings

Lentil Shepherd's Pie, Chickpea Noodle Soup, Oatmeal with Chia Seeds

Ahh, the siren lure of comfort food! Those days when all you crave is a warm hug on a plate. Fear not, for those cravings needn't be weighted down by guilt. Let's delve into delicious and healthy comfort food that'll calm your soul and nourish your body:

**1. Lentil Shepherd's Pie:** A classic reinvented: Swap ground meat for protein-packed lentils. Simmer them in a rich veggie broth with onions, carrots, and herbs. Spoon this delight into a baking dish and top with creamy mashed potatoes made with cauliflower or sweet potatoes for a lighter, fiber-rich twist. Bake till golden brown and bubbling for a cozy symphony of textures and flavors.

**2. Chickpea Noodle Soup:** The ultimate embrace in a bowl: Sauté onions, carrots, and celery in a saucepan. Add your favorite broth, diced tomatoes, and seasonings. Stir in a can of drained and rinsed chickpeas for a hefty protein boost. Let boil until aromatic and then mix in cooked whole-wheat noodles or spiralized zucchini for a healthy twist. This soul-warming soup is sheer comfort on a chilly day.

**3. Oatmeal with Chia Seeds:** The perfect warm breakfast or comforting snack: Cook up a bowl of hearty oatmeal. Stir in a spoonful of chia seeds for an added dose of fiber and omega-3s. Top with your favorite toppings like sliced banana, nuts, berries, a sprinkle of honey, or even nut butter for a creamy twist. This simple yet delightful recipe will start your day off right or curb those afternoon cravings with a taste of nutritious goodness.

**Bonus Tip:** Don't forget the spices! A sprinkling of cumin, turmeric, or smoky paprika can give depth and warmth to any of these meals. And for a touch of luxury, add a dollop of olive oil or sprinkle some cheese on top before baking or eating.

Remember, comfort food is about more than simply ingredients. It's about the warmth, the memories, the sensation of being cared for. So go ahead, indulge in these healthy and tasty versions of your favorites, and embrace the comfort with a smile. Your body and taste buds will appreciate you!

## Salty Snacks

Roasted chickpeas, hummus with veggies, edamame pods

Craving that salty bite but want to escape the guilt trip? Don't worry, your taste buds (and your waistline) can still be happy! Here are some delicious and nutritious salty snacks to satiate your cravings:

**1. Roasted Chickpeas:** Crunchy, protein-packed goodness: Drain and rinse a can of chickpeas, wipe them dry, then combine them with your chosen spices. Think paprika, cumin, chili powder, or even curry powder for a taste experience. Spread them on a baking sheet and roast until golden brown and crispy. Enjoy them hot or cold, single or dipped in hummus for an added flavor punch.

**2. Hummus with Vegetables:** Creamy, delicious dip with veggie power: Make your own hummus with canned chickpeas, tahini, lemon juice, olive oil, and garlic, or purchase a store-bought version rich with good-for-you lipids and protein. Slice up your favorite crunchy vegetables like carrots, bell peppers, cucumber, or celery sticks and dip away! Feel free to add a sprinkle of your favorite nuts or roasted chickpeas for even more texture and flavor.

**3. Edamame Pods:** Soybean pops of perfection: Steam or boil frozen edamame pods until tender-crisp. Sprinkle them with a touch of sea salt and maybe a dab of chili flakes or smoked paprika for a smokey kick. These little green jewels are rich of protein and fiber, making them a delightful and healthful snack on the go.

**Bonus Tips:** Get creative with your seasonings! Experiment with different blends for roasted chickpeas and edamame to keep things interesting.

Make your own veggie chips! Slice sweet potatoes, zucchini, or even beets thinly, mix them with a splash of olive oil and spices, and bake until crispy.

Don't forget the fruit! Pair your salty snacks with fresh fruit slices like apples, pears, or oranges for a sweet and salty balance.

Portion control is crucial! Even healthy snacks can carry a calorie punch, so measure out your quantities to prevent overdoing them.

Remember, salty snacks can be a part of a balanced diet when you choose healthy options. So indulge in those crunchy cravings with ease, knowing you're fuelling your body with goodness!

# Personalizing Your Low GI Diet

## Identifying Your Food Triggers

Identifying your food triggers can be a journey of discovery, but it's a crucial step towards improving your health and well-being. Here are some strategies to help you find those annoying culprits:

### 1. Food & Symptom Diary:

- **Keep a detailed log:** This is the best standard for identifying food triggers. Record everything you eat and drink, along with the time, portion amount, and any symptoms you encounter within the next 24-48 hours. Be descriptive about the symptoms, including their intensity and duration.
- **Patterns emerge:** After a week or two, start looking for trends. Do some meals consistently provoke certain symptoms? Are there any clusters of symptoms that seem to point to specific culprits?
- **Professional guidance:** Consider seeing a trained dietitian or nutritionist to assist understand your diary and recommend additional measures.

### 2. Elimination Diet:

- **Targeted approach:** This strategy entails eliminating probable trigger items from your diet for a defined period, usually 2-6 weeks. Gradually reintroduce them one at a time, monitoring for any responses.
- **Challenges and benefits:** This can be a more complex method, but it can be quite helpful in detecting individual triggers. However, it's crucial to have professional assistance to ensure you're achieving your nutritional needs during the elimination period.

### 3. Food Sensitivity Tests:

- **Blood or skin tests:** These tests examine your body's immunological response to particular foods. While not always definitive, they can provide some hints concerning potential triggers.
- **Consultations:** Don't rely simply on the test results. Discuss them with a doctor or certified dietitian to interpret them in the context of your general health and symptoms.

### 4. Listen to your body:

- **Intuition matters:** Pay attention to how you feel after eating particular foods. Do you feel bloating, gas, headaches, lethargy, or other symptoms? These can be indicators to potential triggers.

- **Experimentation:** Don't be scared to experiment with new foods and see how they effect you. However, avoid radical modifications or eliminating entire dietary groups without professional assistance.

**Remember:** Identifying dietary triggers is a process, not a quick fix. Be patient, consistent, and open to trying alternative ways.

Seek professional help if needed. A doctor, certified dietitian, or nutritionist can provide helpful direction and support along your journey.

Celebrate your progress! Every step you take towards knowing your body and enhancing your health is a victory.

With perseverance and a little detective work, you can identify your food triggers and take charge of your health. Bon appétit!

## Listening to Your Body's Cues

Our bodies are remarkable communication hubs, continually sending us signals about their needs and goals. Learning to listen to these signs is a wonderful tool for improving our physical and emotional well-being. Here are some techniques to tune into your body's whispers and shouts:

**Physical Cues:**

- **Hunger and satiety**: Pay attention to the natural sensations of hunger and fullness. Avoid ignoring hunger pangs or pushing beyond satisfaction to prevent overeating.
- **Energy levels:** Notice changes in your energy throughout the day. A dip around 3 PM can indicate needing a snack, while feeling wired at night could signal insufficient physical activity.
- **Sleepiness:** Yawning, heavy eyelids, and difficulty focusing are your body's way of seeking rest. Don't fight slumber, and emphasize obtaining adequate sleep for maximum functioning.
- **Discomfort:** Listen to aches, pains, and stress. They could be messages regarding posture, injury, or stress needing treatment.
- **Digestive issues:** Bloating, gas, or irregular bowel motions might be indicators of food sensitivities or imbalances. Adjust your diet or visit a healthcare expert if it persists.

**Emotional Cues:**

- **Cravings:** Food cravings can be driven by emotions like stress, boredom, or grief. Pause and ponder before giving in. Is it physical hunger or an emotional urge?
- **Anxiety and stress:** Physical signs including rapid heartbeat, muscle tension, and shallow breathing might signify increased stress. Engage in relaxation techniques like deep breathing or meditation to handle it.
- **Mood swings:** Notice any association between certain foods or activities and changes in your mood. Avoid triggers and prioritize activities that enhance your mood and well-being.

- **Intuition:** Pay heed to gut instincts and a sense of "rightness" or "wrongness" regarding specific actions. Your intuition often whispers vital guidance.

**Tips for Enhanced Listening:**

- **Slow down:** Take time to savor your food, notice flavors, textures, and any bodily feelings.
- **Practice mindfulness:** Engage in meditation or mindful activities to become more aware of your body's internal signals.
- **Keep a journal:** Track your physical and emotional experiences, food consumption, and sleep patterns to uncover any patterns or links.
- **Move your body:** Physical activity helps alleviate tension and enhances the connection between your mind and body.
- **Talk to your body:** Ask yourself questions like "What do I need right now?" or "What message is my body sending me?" Be receptive to receive the answers.

Remember, listening to your body is a journey, not a destination. Be patient, practice consistently, and applaud your improvement. As you improve your connection with your inner knowledge, you'll make decisions that match with your genuine needs and uncover a road to optimal health and well-being. Your body knows the way, just start listening!

## Finding Healthy Swaps that Work for You

Making healthy changes can seem difficult, but it's all about finding solutions that work for you! Here are some ideas to traverse the swap zone and make durable adjustments that taste delicious and feel good:

**Start small:** Don't overload yourself by trying to alter everything at once. Pick one or two things you wish to tweak in your diet and focus on those. For example, change sugary sodas for sparkling water with fruit slices or replace white bread with whole-wheat choices.

**Consider your taste:** Choose swaps that you'll genuinely enjoy. If you detest kale, don't push yourself to eat it just because it's healthful. There are plenty of other great vegetables out there! Experiment and find substitutes that you actually find tasty.

**Think beyond the box:** Don't limit yourself to obvious swaps. Try replacing ground beef with lentils in your favorite lasagna, substitute fried chicken for baked tofu nuggets, or use mashed sweet potatoes instead of mashed white potatoes for a healthy and delectable twist.

**Make it convenient:** Choose swaps that are easy to implement into your lifestyle. If you're short on time, pre-washed and chopped vegetables can be a terrific substitute for raw ones. Opt for frozen fruits and veggies when fresh ones aren't in season.

**Don't demonize treats:** It's alright to indulge in your favorite delicacies periodically. Instead of fully eliminating them, choose healthier alternatives you can enjoy more regularly. For example, substitute store-bought cookies with homemade oatmeal cookies made with whole wheat flour and natural sugars.

**Get creative with spices and herbs:** Spices and herbs can add plenty of flavor to your cuisine, making healthy substitutions much more enticing. Experiment with different combinations to find ones you prefer.

**Make it a family affair:** Get your family engaged in making healthy swaps. Let them choose some substitutes they'd like to explore and make it an enjoyable learning experience.

Remember, progress, not perfection is key: Don't beat yourself up if you slip up here and then. The key thing is to keep moving forward and creating positive changes, one step at a time.

## Making Low GI a Flexible Lifestyle

Living a low GI lifestyle doesn't have to be restricted or boring! Embrace flexibility and make it sustainable for the long haul with these tips:

**1. Focus on the larger picture:** Don't stress over every single meal or snack. Aim for an overall low GI diet with occasional treats or higher GI foods enjoyed in moderation.

**2. Prioritize whole foods:** Fill your plate with fruits, vegetables, whole grains, legumes, and lean protein. These low GI superstars keep you feeling full and energized.

**3. Get creative with swaps:** Replace refined carbs with whole-wheat alternatives, sugary drinks with water and herbal teas, and processed nibbles with nuts, seeds, and fruits.

**4. Embrace variety:** Don't get stuck in a rut! Explore different low GI foods and cuisines to keep things interesting and reduce cravings.

**5. Cook at home:** Having control over ingredients enables you adapt your meals to your low GI demands. Plus, it's generally cheaper and healthier than eating out.

**6. Plan ahead:** Meal planning and grocery shopping make it simpler to keep to your low GI plan, even on hectic days.

**7. Listen to your body:** Pay attention to hunger and fullness cues, and avoid restricted or fad diets. A balanced, low GI approach is crucial to long-term success.

**8. Enjoy your food:** Food should be a source of pleasure, not worry. Savor your meals, experiment with flavors, and don't deny yourself of occasional delights.

**9. Be aware of portions:** Even low GI foods can be enjoyed in excess. Practice mindful eating and regulate portion sizes to avoid overindulging.

**10. Appreciate progress:** Focus on the good improvements you're making and appreciate your triumphs, big or small. Remember, making durable changes takes time and effort, so be nice to yourself along the way.

**Bonus Tip:** Find a low GI buddy or community for support and encouragement. Sharing your trip might make it more exciting and fulfilling.

Making a low GI lifestyle flexible isn't about perfection, it's about finding a balance that works for you. Experiment, listen to your body, and enjoy the tasty and healthy adventure!

Remember, a flexible low GI strategy can become a gateway to a healthier, happier, and more energetic existence. So, embrace the freedom, develop your culinary creativity, and relish the adventure!

# WEEKLY MEAL PLAN

|  | BREAKFAST | LUNCH | DINNER | SNACKS/DESSERT |
|--|-----------|-------|--------|----------------|
|  |           |       |        |                |

| | | | | |
|---|---|---|---|---|
| SUNDAY | | | | |
| MONDAY | | | | |
| TUESDAY | | | | |
| WEDNESDAY | | | | |
| THURSDAY | | | | |
| FRIDAY | | | | |
| SATURDAY | | | | |

# BONUS: 14-DAY DETAILED LOW GI MEAL PLAN

This plan incorporates recipes mentioned previously while offering variety and flexibility. Remember to adjust portion sizes and snacks based on your individual needs and preferences.

**Day 1:**

**Breakfast:** Greek yogurt with berries and chia seeds
**Lunch:** Quinoa salad with roasted chickpeas, avocado, and balsamic vinaigrette
**Dinner:** Slow cooker lentil soup with whole-wheat

**Day 2:**

**Breakfast:** Omelette with spinach, mushrooms, and low-fat cheese
**Lunch:** Leftover lentil soup with a side salad
**Dinner:** Salmon with roasted sweet potatoes and green

**Day 3:**

**Breakfast:** Oatmeal with nuts and seeds

**Lunch:** Turkey and vegetable wrap on whole-wheat tortillas

**Dinner:** One-pan chicken stir-fry with brown rice and peppers

**Day 4:**

**Breakfast:** Chia pudding with fruit and nuts
**Lunch:** Leftover stir-fry with a side of cucumber and tomato salad
**Dinner:** Vegetarian chili with cornbread muffins

**Day 5:**

**Breakfast:** Egg muffins with spinach and peppers
**Lunch:** Tuna salad with apple slices and crackers
**Dinner:** Baked tofu with quinoa and roasted Brussels sprouts

**Day 6 (Rest & Recuperation):**

**Breakfast:** Smoothie bowl with frozen fruit, spinach, and granola
**Lunch:** Leftover vegetarian chili
**Dinner:** Lentil Shepherd's Pie

Day 7:

**Breakfast:** Pancakes made with whole-wheat flour and fruit topping
**Lunch:** Chickpea Noodle Soup with whole-wheat bread
**Dinner:** Roasted cod with steamed vegetables and brown rice

Day 8:

**Breakfast:** Oatmeal with a drizzle of honey and chopped nuts
**Lunch:** Salad with quinoa, grilled chicken, and avocado
**Dinner:** Vegetable curry with brown rice and naan

Day 9:

**Breakfast:** Scrambled eggs with smoked salmon and whole-wheat toast
**Lunch:** Leftover vegetable curry
**Dinner:** Black bean burgers on whole-wheat buns with sweet potato fries and salad

Day 10:

**Breakfast:** Fruit salad with yogurt and granola
**Lunch:** Tuna salad sandwich on whole-wheat bread with sliced vegetables
**Dinner:** Chicken stir-fry with broccoli and brown rice

Day 12:

**Breakfast:** Whole-wheat pancakes with berries and Greek yogurt
**Lunch:** Leftover lentil salad with a side salad
**Dinner:** Vegetarian chili with cornbread muffins

Day 13:

**Breakfast:** Chia pudding with fruit and nuts
**Lunch:** Turkey and vegetable wrap on whole-wheat tortillas
**Dinner:** One-pan chicken stir-fry with brown rice and peppers

Day 14:

**Breakfast:** Greek yogurt with berries and chia seeds
**Lunch:** Quinoa salad with roasted chickpeas, avocado, and balsamic
**Dinner:** Slow cooker lentil soup with whole-wheat bread

**Snacks:** Throughout the day, enjoy healthy snacks like fruits, vegetables, nuts, seeds, yogurt, hard-boiled eggs, low-fat cheese, or hummus with vegetables. Remember to choose low GI options for optimal blood sugar control.

This is just a sample plan, feel free to mix and match recipes, create your own variations, and adapt it to your preferences and dietary needs. Enjoy your delicious and healthy low GI journey!

# Index of Recipes and Ingredients

Recipes:

Batch Cooking Techniques:

- Double or triple recipes
- Master the base recipe
- Go for grains in bulk
- Roast it up

Low GI Meal Prep Ideas for the Week:

Monday:

- Breakfast: Chia pudding with berries and nuts
- Lunch: Salad with quinoa, roasted chickpeas, avocado, and balsamic vinaigrette
- Dinner: Slow cooker lentil soup with whole-wheat bread

Tuesday:

- Breakfast: Omelette with spinach, mushrooms, and low-fat cheese
- Lunch: Leftover lentil soup with a side salad
- Dinner: Salmon with roasted sweet potatoes and green beans

Wednesday:

- Breakfast: Oatmeal with nuts and seeds
- Lunch: Turkey and vegetable wrap on whole-wheat tortillas
- Dinner: One-pan chicken stir-fry with brown rice and peppers

Thursday:

- Breakfast: Chia pudding with fruit and nuts
- Lunch: Leftover stir-fry with a side of cucumber and tomato salad
- Dinner: Vegetarian chili with cornbread muffins

Friday:

- Breakfast: Egg muffins with spinach and peppers
- Lunch: Tuna salad with apple slices and crackers
- Dinner: Baked tofu with quinoa and roasted Brussels sprouts

Satisfying Sweets:

- Fruit with yogurt, dark chocolate, homemade energy bites

- Dark Chocolate Dipped Dates with Almond Butter
- Tropical Smoothie Bowl with Homemade Granola
- Homemade Energy Bites
- Baked Apples with Cinnamon and Walnuts

Comfort Food Cravings:

- Lentil Shepherd's Pie
- Chickpea Noodle Soup
- Oatmeal with Chia Seeds

Salty Snacks:

- Roasted Chickpeas
- Hummus with Vegetables
- Edamame Pods

Ingredients:

- Fruits: apples, bananas, berries, dates, mango, pineapple, pears
- Vegetables: avocado, bell peppers, broccoli, Brussels sprouts, carrots, celery, chickpeas, cucumber, green beans, onions, spinach, sweet potatoes, tomatoes
- Grains and Legumes: brown rice, cornbread muffins, lentils, oats, quinoa, tofu, whole-wheat bread, whole-wheat tortillas
- Protein: almonds, chicken, cod, eggs, nuts, salmon, seeds, turkey
- Dairy and Alternatives: cheese, Greek yogurt, hummus, nut butter, plant-based yogurt
- Sweeteners: chia seeds, dark chocolate, honey, natural sweeteners
- Spices and Herbs: basil, chili flakes, cinnamon, cumin, curry powder, paprika, sea salt, smoked paprika, turmeric
- Other: chia seeds, coconut flakes, coconut yogurt, granola, olive oil, tahini, vegetable broth

This is not an exhaustive list, but it covers the main ingredients included in the recipes mentioned above. Please note that specific quantities and variations may differ depending on the chosen recipe.

I hope this index helps you easily find the information you need when exploring these recipes and planning your meals!

Made in United States
Troutdale, OR
04/13/2024